OPENING WORLDS
short stories from different cultures

For use with OCR examinations
GCSE English and English Literature 2003 – 2008

OCR (Oxford Cambridge and RSA Examinations)
1 Hill Road, Cambridge CB1 2EU

© Oxford Cambridge and RSA Examinations 2002

10-digit ISBN 0 435 150952
13-digit ISBN 978 0 435150 95 2
Produced by Heinemann Educational

Designed and typeset by Jackie Hill 320 Design

Cover photographs: Woman: Eye Ubiquitous/Bennet Dean; Oak tree: Hutchison Library/
Edward Parker; Cricket ball: Getty Images/Image Bank; Frog: Getty Images/Image Bank

Cover design by hicksdesign

Printed and bound in Great Britain by Thomson Litho, East Kilbride, Scotland

The publisher would like to thank the following for permission to reproduce photgraphs
on the pages noted:
Camera Press/Miriam Berkley (p.6); Camera Press (p.10); Camera Press/John Reardon
(p.16); Art and Culture Magazine, Matichon Group, Thailand (p.22); Corbis/Reuters
NewMedia Inc. (p.29); © 2000 Enorth.co.cn, Tianjin Enorth NetNews Co.Ltd. (p.41); Trevor
Sealy (p.51); Peepal Tree Press (p.59); Camera Press/Jane Bown (p.68); Shiel Land
Associates (p.83); Camera Press (p.89); Camera Press (p.97).

This book is dedicated
to the memory of
Ian Barr
(1941–2001)
whose idea it was

CONTENTS

INTRODUCTION

Opening Worlds is a collection of short stories from different cultures and traditions. Each story has been set for study in previous OCR examinations. All have been enjoyed, both by students and by their teachers. They are now collected into a single volume, to meet the requirements of the new GCSE specifications for examination from June 2003 onwards.

GCSE English Literature

Examinations
Opening Worlds is set as an optional Post-1914 prose text for examinations in OCR GCSE English Literature from June 2003 onwards. For examinations in English Literature, the complete collection is set for study.

Coursework
Any of the stories included in *Opening Worlds* may be studied for English Literature coursework, as appropriate to the specification requirements.

GCSE English

Examinations
Opening Worlds is set as an optional text for examinations in OCR GCSE English Unit 2 from June 2003 onwards.

For full details of examination requirements, please refer to the specification booklets.

Chinua Achebe

NIGERIA

Dead Men's Path

Chinua Achebe was born in Ogidi, Nigeria, in 1930, the son of devout evangelical Protestants. He has travelled widely and is now a famous novelist, poet, story-writer, broadcaster and teacher. His work has had a dramatic impact on the development of literature in Africa and often explores the effects of European customs and beliefs on traditional African society.

Michael Obi's hopes were fulfilled much earlier than he had expected. He was appointed headmaster of Ndume Central School in January 1949. It had always been an unprogressive school, so the Mission authorities decided to send a young and
5   energetic man to run it. Obi accepted this responsibility with enthusiasm. He had many wonderful ideas and this was an opportunity to put them into practice. He had had sound secondary school education which designated him a 'pivotal teacher' in the official records and set him apart from the other headmasters in the
10 mission field. He was outspoken in his condemnation of the narrow views of these older and often less-educated ones.

'We shall make a good job of it, shan't we?' he asked his young wife when they first heard the joyful news of his promotion.

'We shall do our best,' she replied. 'We shall have such beautiful
15 gardens and everything will be just *modern* and delightful . . .' In their two years of married life she had become completely infected by his passion for 'modern methods' and his denigration of 'these old and superannuated people in the teaching field who would be better employed as traders in the Onitsha market'. She began to see herself
20 already as the admired wife of the young headmaster, the queen of the school.

The wives of the other teachers would envy her position. She would set the fashion in everything . . . Then, suddenly, it occurred to her that there might not be other wives. Wavering between hope and

25 fear, she asked her husband, looking anxiously at him.

'All our colleagues are young and unmarried,' he said with enthusiasm which for once she did not share. 'Which is a good thing,' he continued.

'Why?'

30 'Why? They will give all their time and energy to the school.'

Nancy was downcast. For a few minutes she became sceptical about the new school; but it was only for a few minutes. Her little personal misfortune could not blind her to her husband's happy prospects. She looked at him as he sat folded up in a chair. He was

35 stoop-shouldered and looked frail. But he sometimes surprised people with sudden bursts of physical energy. In his present posture, however, all his bodily strength seemed to have retired behind his deep-set eyes, giving them an extraordinary power of penetration. He was only twenty-six, but looked thirty or more. On the whole, he was

40 not unhandsome.

'A penny for your thoughts, Mike,' said Nancy after a while, imitating the woman's magazine she read.

'I was thinking what a grand opportunity we've got at last to show these people how a school should be run.' Ndume School was

45 backward in every sense of the word. Mr Obi put his whole life into the work, and his wife hers too. He had two aims. A high standard of teaching was insisted upon, and the school compound was to be turned into a place of beauty. Nancy's dream-gardens came to life with the coming of the rains, and blossomed. Beautiful hibiscus and

50 allamanda hedges in brilliant red and yellow marked out carefully tended school compound from the rank neighbourhood bushes.

One evening as Obi was admiring his work he was scandalized to see an old woman from the village hobble right across the compound, through a marigold flower-bed and the hedges. On going up there he

55 found faint signs of an almost disused path from the village across the school compound to the bush on the other side.

'It amazes me,' said Obi to one of his teachers who had been three years in the school, 'that you people allowed the villagers to make use of this footpath. It is simply incredible.' He shook his head.

60 'The path,' said the teacher apologetically, 'appears to be very

important to them. Although it is hardly used, it connects the village shrine with their place of burial.'

'And what has that got to do with the school?' asked the headmaster.

'Well, I don't know,' replied the other with a shrug of the shoulders. 'But I remember there was a big row some time ago when we attempted to close it.'

'That was some time ago. But it will not be used now,' said Obi as he walked away. 'What will the Government Education Officer think of this when he comes to inspect the school next week? The villagers might, for all I know, decide to use the schoolroom for a pagan ritual during the inspection.'

Heavy sticks were planted closely across the path at the two places where it entered and left the school premises. These were further strengthened with barbed wire.

Three days later the village priest of *Ani* called on the headmaster. He was an old man and walked with a slight stoop. He carried a stout walking-stick which he usually tapped on the floor, by way of emphasis, each time he made a new point in his argument.

'I have heard,' he said after the usual exchange of cordialities, 'that our ancestral footpath has recently been closed . . .'

'Yes,' replied Mr Obi. 'We cannot allow people to make a highway of our school compound.'

'Look here, my son,' said the priest bringing down his walking-stick, 'this path was here before you were born and before your father was born. The whole life of this village depends on it. Our dead relatives depart by it and our ancestors visit us by it. But most important, it is the path of children coming in to be born . . .'

Mr Obi listened with a satisfied smile on his face.

'The whole purpose of our school,' he said finally, 'is to eradicate just such beliefs as that. Dead men do not require footpaths. The whole idea is just fantastic. Our duty is to teach your children to laugh at such ideas.'

'What you say may be true,' replied the priest, 'but we follow the practices of our fathers. If you re-open the path we shall have nothing

to quarrel about. What I always say is: let the hawk perch and let the
eagle perch.' He rose to go.

'I am sorry,' said the young headmaster. 'But the school compound
cannot be a thoroughfare. It is against our regulations. I would
100 suggest your constructing another path, skirting our premises. We can
even get our boys to help in building it. I don't suppose the ancestors
will find the little detour too burdensome.'

'I have no more words to say,' said the old priest, already outside.

Two days later a young woman in the village died in childbed. A
105 diviner was immediately consulted and he prescribed heavy sacrifices
to propitiate ancestors insulted by the fence.

Obi woke up next morning among the ruins of his work. The
beautiful hedges were torn up not just near the path but right round
the school, the flowers trampled to death and one of the school
110 buildings pulled down . . . That day, the white Supervisor came to
inspect the school and wrote a nasty report on the state of the
premises but more seriously about the 'tribal-war situation developing
between the school and the village, arising in part from the misguided
zeal of the new headmaster'.

Bessie Head

Snapshots of a Wedding

Bessie Head was born in South Africa in 1937 to a black father and a white mother. As a consequence of apartheid she was fostered and attended a mission school, before training to become a teacher. She took up permanent exile in Botswana, and became a citizen in 1979. Botswana was the setting for her three novels, and she also wrote a number of short stories and autobiographical pieces. She died in 1986.

Wedding days always started at the haunting, magical hour of early dawn when there was only a pale crack of light on the horizon. For those who were awake, it took the earth hours to adjust to daylight. The cool and damp of the night
5 slowly arose in shimmering waves like water and even the forms of the people who bestirred themselves at this unearthly hour were distorted in the haze; they appeared to be dancers in slow motion, with fluid, watery forms. In the dim light, four men, the relatives of the bridegroom, Kegoletile, slowly herded an ox before them towards
10 the yard of MmaKhudu, where the bride, Neo, lived. People were already astir in MmaKhudu's yard, yet for a while they all came and peered closely at the distorted fluid forms that approached, to ascertain if it were indeed the relatives of the bridegroom. Then the ox, who was a rather stupid fellow and unaware of his sudden and
15 impending end as meat for the wedding feast, bellowed casually his early morning yawn. At this, the beautiful ululating of the women rose and swelled over the air like water bubbling rapidly and melodiously over the stones of a clear, sparkling stream. In between ululating all the while, the women began to weave about the yard in the wedding
20 dance; now and then they bent over and shook their buttocks in the air. As they handed over the ox, one of the bridegroom's relatives joked:

    'This is going to be a modern wedding.' He meant that a lot of the traditional courtesies had been left out of the planning for the

25 wedding day; no one had been awake all night preparing diphiri or the traditional wedding breakfast of pounded meat and samp; the bridegroom said he had no church and did not care about such things; the bride was six months pregnant and showing it, so there was just going to be a quick marriage ceremony at the police camp.

30   'Oh, we all have our own ways,' one of the bride's relatives joked back. 'If the times are changing, we keep up with them.' And she weaved away ululating joyously.

     Whenever there was a wedding the talk and gossip that preceded it were appalling, except that this time the relatives of the 35 bride, Neo, kept their talk a strict secret among themselves. They were anxious to be rid of her; she was an impossible girl with haughty, arrogant ways. Of all her family and relatives, she was the only one who had completed her 'O' levels and she never failed to rub in this fact. She walked around with her nose in the air; 40 illiterate relatives were beneath her greeting – it was done in a clever way, she just turned her head to one side and smiled to herself or when she greeted it was like an insult; she stretched her hand out, palm outspread, swung it down laughing with a gesture that plainly said: 'Oh, that's you!' Only her mother seemed bemused 45 by her education. At her own home Neo was waited on hand and foot. Outside her home nasty remarks were passed. People bitterly disliked conceit and pride.

     'That girl has no manners!' the relatives would remark. 'What's the good of education if it goes to someone's head so badly they 50 have no respect for the people? Oh, she is not a person.'

     Then they would nod their heads in that fatal way, with predictions that one day life would bring her down. Actually, life had treated Neo rather nicely. Two months after completing her 'O' levels she became pregnant by Kegoletile with their first child. It 55 soon became known that another girl, Mathata, was also pregnant by Kegoletile. The difference between the two girls was that Mathata was completely uneducated; the only work she would ever · do was that of a housemaid, while Neo had endless opportunities before her – typist, book-keeper, or secretary. So Neo merely 60 smiled; Mathata was no rival. It was as though the decision had

been worked out by circumstance because when the families converged on Kegoletile at the birth of the children – he was rich in cattle and they wanted to see what they could get – he of course immediately proposed marriage to Neo; and for Mathata, he agreed to
65   a court order to pay a maintenance of R10.00 a month until the child was twenty years old. Mathata merely smiled too. Girls like her offered no resistance to the approaches of men; when they lost them, they just let things ride.

'He is of course just running after the education and not the
70   manners,' Neo's relatives commented, to show they were not fooled by human nature. 'He thinks that since she is as educated as he is they will both get good jobs and be rich in no time . . .'

Educated as he was, Kegoletile seemed to go through a secret conflict during that year he prepared a yard for his future married life
75   with Neo. He spent most of his free time in the yard of Mathata. His behaviour there wasn't too alarming but he showered Mathata with gifts of all kinds – food, fancy dresses, shoes and underwear. Each time he came, he brought a gift and each time Mathata would burst out laughing and comment: 'Ow, Kegoletile, how can I wear all these
80   dresses? It's just a waste of money! Besides, I manage quite well with the R10.00 you give every month for the child . . .'

She was a very pretty girl with black eyes like stars; she was always smiling and happy; immediately and always her own natural self. He knew what he was marrying – something quite the opposite,
85   a new kind of girl with false postures and acquired, grand-madame ways. And yet, it didn't pay a man these days to look too closely into his heart. They all wanted as wives, women who were big money-earners and they were so ruthless about it! And yet it was as though the society itself stamped each of its individuals with its own
90   particular brand of wealth and Kegoletile had not yet escaped it; he had about him an engaging humility and eagerness to help and please that made him loved and respected by all who knew him. During those times he sat in Mathata's yard, he communicated nothing of the conflict he felt but he would sit on a chair with his arms spread out
95   across its back, turn his head sideways and stare at what seemed to be an empty space beside him. Then he would smile, stand up and

walk away. Nothing dramatic. During the year he prepared the huts in his new yard, he frequently slept at the home of Neo.

Relatives on both sides watched this division of interest between the two yards and one day when Neo walked patronizingly into the yard of an aunt, the aunt decided to frighten her a little.

'Well aunt,' she said, with the familiar careless disrespect which went with her so-called, educated, status. 'Will you make me some tea? And how's things?'

The aunt spoke very quietly.

'You may not know it, my girl, but you are hated by everyone around here. The debate we have going is whether a nice young man like Kegoletile should marry bad-mannered rubbish like you. He would be far better off if he married a girl like Mathata, who though uneducated, still treats people with respect.'

The shock the silly girl received made her stare for a terrified moment at her aunt. Then she stood up and ran out of the house. It wiped the superior smile off her face and brought her down a little. She developed an anxiety to greet people and also an anxiety about securing Kegoletile as a husband – that was why she became pregnant six months before the marriage could take place. In spite of this, her own relatives still disliked her and right up to the day of the wedding they were still debating whether Neo was a suitable wife for any man. No one would have guessed it though with all the dancing, ululating and happiness expressed in the yard and streams of guests gaily ululated themselves along the pathways with wedding gifts precariously balanced on their heads. Neo's maternal aunts, all sedately decked up in shawls, sat in a select group by themselves in a corner of the yard. They sat on the bare ground with their legs stretched out before them but they were served like queens the whole day long. Trays of tea, dry white bread, plates of meat, rice, and salad were constantly placed before them. Their important task was to formally hand over the bride to Kegoletile's maternal aunts when they approached the yard at sunset. So they sat the whole day with still, expressionless faces, waiting to fulfil this ancient rite.

Equally still and expressionless were the faces of the long column of women, Kegoletile's maternal aunts, who appeared outside the yard just as the sun sank low. They walked slowly into the yard indifferent to the ululating that greeted them and seated themselves in

135   a group opposite Neo's maternal aunts. The yard became very silent while each group made its report. Kegoletile had provided all the food for the wedding feast and a maternal aunt from his side first asked:

'Is there any complaint? Has all gone well?'

140   'We have no complaint,' the opposite party replied.

'We have come to ask for water,' Kegoletile's side said, meaning that from times past the bride was supposed to carry water at her in-law's home.

'It is agreed to,' the opposite party replied.

145   Neo's maternal aunts then turned to the bridegroom and counselled him: 'Son, you must plough and supply us with corn each year.'

Then Kegoletile's maternal aunts turned to the bride and counselled her: 'Daughter, you must carry water for your husband.

150   Beware, that at all times, he is the owner of the house and must be obeyed. Do not mind if he stops now and then and talks to other ladies. Let him feel free to come and go as he likes . . .'

The formalities over, it was now time for Kegoletile's maternal aunts to get up, ululate and weave and dance about the yard. Then,

155   still dancing and ululating, accompanied by the bride and groom they slowly wound their way to the yard of Kegoletile where another feast had been prepared. As they approached his yard, an old woman suddenly dashed out and chopped at the ground with a hoe. It was all only a formality. Neo would never be the kind of wife who went

160   to the lands to plough. She already had a well-paid job in an office as a secretary. Following on this another old woman took the bride by the hand and led her to a smeared and decorated courtyard wherein had been placed a traditional animal-skin Tswana mat. She was made to sit on the mat and a shawl and kerchief were placed before her.

165   The shawl was ceremonially wrapped around her shoulders; the kerchief tied around her head – the symbols that she was now a married woman.

Guests quietly moved forward to greet the bride. Then two girls

started to ululate and dance in front of the bride. As they both turned
170 and bent over to shake their buttocks in the air, they bumped into
each other and toppled over. The wedding guests roared with
laughter. Neo, who had all this time been stiff, immobile, and rigid,
bent forward and her shoulders shook with laughter.

The hoe, the mat, the shawl, the kerchief, the beautiful flute-like
175 ululating of the women seemed in itself a blessing on the marriage
but all the guests were deeply moved when out of the crowd, a
woman of majestic, regal bearing slowly approached the bride. It was
the aunt who had scolded Neo for her bad manners and modern
ways. She dropped to her knees before the bride, clenched her fists
180 together and pounded the ground hard with each clenched fist on
either side of the bride's legs. As she pounded her fists she said
loudly:

'Be a good wife! Be a good wife!'

Nadine Gordimer

The Train from Rhodesia

Nadine Gordimer was born into a well-off family in a mining town outside Johannesburg, South Africa, in 1923. She began writing at the age of nine and her first story, 'Come Again Tomorrow', appeared in print when she was only fourteen. Her writing deals with the moral and psychological tensions of her racially divided home country. Gordimer was a founding member of the Congress of South African Writers, and received the Nobel Prize for Literature in 1991.

The train came out of the red horizon and bore down towards them over the single straight track.

The stationmaster came out of his little brick station with its pointed chalet roof, feeling the creases in his serge uniform in his legs as well.
5   A stir of preparedness rippled through the squatting native venders waiting in the dust; the face of a carved wooden animal, eternally surprised, stuck out of a sack. The stationmaster's barefoot children wandered over. From the grey mud huts with the untidy heads that stood within a decorated mud wall, chickens, and dogs with their skin
10 stretched like parchment over their bones, followed the piccanins down to the track. The flushed and perspiring west cast a reflection, faint, without heat, upon the station, upon the tin shed marked 'Goods', upon the walled kraal, upon the grey tin house of the stationmaster and upon the sand, that lapped all around, from sky to
15 sky, cast little rhythmical cups of shadow, so that the sand became the sea, and closed over the children's black feet softly and without imprint.
        The stationmaster's wife sat behind the mesh of her veranda. Above her head the hunk of a sheep's carcass moved slightly,
20 dangling in a current of air.
        They waited.
        The train called out, along the sky; but there was no answer; and

the cry hung on: I'm coming . . . I'm coming . . .

The engine flared out now, big, whisking a dwindling body
25 behind it; the track flared out to let it in.

Creaking, jerking, jostling, gasping, the train filled the station.

Here, let me see that one – the young woman curved her body farther
out of the corridor window. Missus? smiled the old man, looking at
the creatures he held in his hand. From a piece of string on his grey
30 finger hung a tiny woven basket; he lifted it, questioning. No, no, she
urged, leaning down towards him, across the height of the train
towards the man in the piece of old rug; that one, that one, her hand
commanded. It was a lion, carved out of soft dry wood that looked
like spongecake; heraldic, black and white, with impressionistic detail
35 burnt in. The old man held it up to her still smiling, not from the
heart, but at the customer. Between its vandyke teeth, in the mouth
opened in an endless roar too terrible to be heard, it had a black
tongue. Look, said the young husband, if you don't mind! And round
the neck of the thing, a piece of fur (rat? rabbit? meerkat?); a real
40 mane, majestic, telling you somehow that the artist had delight in the
lion.

All up and down the length of the train in the dust the artists
sprang, walking bent, like performing animals, the better to exhibit
the fantasy held towards the faces on the train. Buck, startled and stiff,
45 staring with round black and white eyes. More lions, standing erect,
grappling with strange, thin, elongated warriors who clutched spears
and showed no fear in their slits of eyes. How much, they asked from
the train, how much?

Give me penny, said the little ones with nothing to sell. The dogs
50 went and sat, quite still, under the dining car, where the train
breathed out the smell of meat cooking with onion.

A man passed beneath the arch of reaching arms meeting grey-
black and white in the exchange of money for the staring wooden
eyes, the stiff wooden legs sticking up in the air; went along under
55 the voices and the bargaining, interrogating the wheels. Past the dogs;
glancing up at the dining car where he could stare at the faces,
behind glass, drinking beer, two by two, on either side of a uniform

railway vase with its pale dead flower. Right to the end, to the guard's
van, where the stationmaster's children had just collected their
60   mother's two loaves of bread; to the engine itself, where the
stationmaster and the driver stood talking against the steaming
complaint of the resting beast.

    The man called out to them, something loud and joking. They
turned to laugh, in a twirl of steam. The two children careered over
65   the sand, clutching the bread, and burst through the iron gate and up
the path through the garden in which nothing grew.

    Passengers drew themselves in at the corridor windows and turned
into compartments to fetch money, to call someone to look. Those
sitting inside looked up: suddenly different, caged faces, boxed in, cut
70   off after the contact of outside. There was an orange a piccanin would
like . . . What about that chocolate? It wasn't very nice . . .

    A girl had collected a handful of the hard kind, that no one liked,
out of the chocolate box, and was throwing them to the dogs, over at
the dining car. But the hens darted in and swallowed the chocolates,
75   incredibly quick and accurate, before they had even dropped in the
dust, and the dogs, a little bewildered, looked up with their brown
eyes, not expecting anything.

    – No, leave it, said the young woman, don't take it . . .

    Too expensive, too much, she shook her head and raised her
80   voice to the old man, giving up the lion. He held it high where she
had handed it to him. No, she said, shaking her head. Three-and-six?
insisted her husband, loudly. Yes baas! laughed the old man. *Three-
and-six?* – the young man was incredulous. Oh leave it – she said.
The young man stopped. Don't you want it? he said, keeping his face
85   closed to the old man. No, never mind, she said, leave it. The old
native kept his head on one side, looking at them sideways, holding
the lion. Three-and-six, he murmured, as old people repeat things to
themselves.

    The young woman drew her head in. She went into the coupé and
90   sat down. Out of the window, on the other side, there was nothing;
sand and bush; a thorn tree. Back through the open doorway, past
the figure of her husband in the corridor, there was the station, the
voices, wooden animals waving, running feet. Her eye followed the

funny little valance of scrolled wood that outlined the chalet roof of
95   the station; she thought of the lion and smiled. That bit of fur round
the neck. But the wooden buck, the hippos, the elephants, the
baskets that already bulked out of their brown paper under the seat
and on the luggage rack! How will they look at home? Where will you
put them? What will they mean away from the places you found
100   them? Away from the unreality of the last few weeks? The young man
outside. But he is not part of the unreality; he is for good now. Odd
. . . somewhere there was an idea that he, that living with him, was
part of the holiday, the strange places.

Outside, a bell rang. The stationmaster was leaning against the end
105   of the train, green flag rolled in readiness. A few men who had got
down to stretch their legs sprang on to the train, clinging to the
observation platforms, or perhaps merely standing on the iron step,
holding the rail; but on the train, safe from the one dusty platform,
the one tin house, the empty sand.

110   There was a grunt. The train jerked. Through the glass the beer
drinkers looked out, as if they could not see beyond it. Behind the
fly-screen, the stationmaster's wife sat facing back at them beneath the
darkening hunk of meat.

There was a shout. The flag drooped out. Joints not yet
115   coordinated, the segmented body of the train heaved and bumped
back against itself. It began to move; slowly the scrolled chalet moved
past it, the yells of the natives, running alongside, jetted up into the
air, fell back at different levels. Staring wooden faces waved
drunkenly, there, then gone, questioning for the last time at the
120   windows. Here, one-and-six baas! – As one automatically opens a
hand to catch a thrown ball, a man fumbled wildly down his pocket,
brought up the shilling and sixpence and threw them out; the old
native, gasping, his skinny toes splaying the sand, flung the lion.

The piccanins were waving, the dogs stood, tails uncertain,
125   watching the train go: past the mud huts, where a woman turned to
look up from the smoke of the fire, her hand pausing on her hip.

The stationmaster went slowly in under the chalet.

The old native stood, breath blowing out the skin between his
ribs, feet tense, balanced in the sand, smiling and shaking his head. In

130 his opened palm, held in the attitude of receiving, was the retrieved shilling and sixpence.

 The blind end of the train was being pulled helplessly out of the station.

The young man swung in from the corridor, breathless. He was
135 shaking his head with laughter and triumph. Here! he said. And waggled the lion at her. One-and-six!

 What? she said.

 He laughed. I was arguing with him for fun, bargaining – when the train had pulled out already, he came tearing after . . . One-and-six
140 Baas! So there's your lion.

 She was holding it away from her, the head with the open jaws, the pointed teeth, the black tongue, the wonderful ruff of fur facing her. She was looking at it with an expression of not seeing, of seeing something different. Her face was drawn up, wryly, like the face of a
145 discomforted child. Her mouth lifted nervously at the corner. Very slowly, cautious, she lifted her finger and touched the mane, where it was joined to the wood.

 But how could you, she said. He was shocked by the dismay of her face.

150 Good Lord, he said, what's the matter?

 If you wanted the thing, she said, her voice rising and breaking with the shrill impotence of anger, why didn't you buy it in the first place? If you wanted it, why didn't you pay for it? Why didn't you take it decently, when he offered it? Why did you have to wait for
155 him to run after the train with it, and give him one-and-six? One-and-six!

 She was pushing it at him, trying to force him to take the lion. He stood astonished, his hands hanging at his sides.

 But you wanted it! You liked it so much?
160 – It's a beautiful piece of work, she said fiercely, as if to protect it from him.

 You liked it so much! You said yourself it was too expensive –

 Oh you – she said, hopeless and furious. You . . . She threw the lion onto the seat.

165　　He stood looking at her.

　　She sat down again in the corner and, her face slumped in her hands, stared out of the window. Everything was turning round inside her. One-and-six. One-and-six. One-and-six for the wood and the carving and the sinews of the legs and the switch of the tail. The

170　mouth open like that and the teeth. The black tongue, rolling, like a wave. The mane round the neck. To give one-and-six for that. The heat of shame mounted through her legs and body and sounded in her ears like the sound of sand pouring. Pouring, pouring. She sat there, sick. A weariness, a tastelessness, the discovery of a void made

175　her hands slacken their grip, atrophy emptily, as if the hour was not worth their grasp. She was feeling like this again. She had thought it was something to do with singleness, with being alone and belonging too much to oneself.

　　She sat there not wanting to move or speak, or to look at anything

180　even; so that the mood should be associated with nothing, no object, word or sight that might recur and so recall the feeling again . . . Smuts blew in grittily, settled on her hands. Her back remained at exactly the same angle, turned against the young man sitting with his hands drooping between his sprawled legs, and the lion, fallen on its

185　side in the corner.

The train had cast the station like a skin. It called out to the sky, I'm coming, I'm coming; and again, there was no answer.

Khamsing Srinawk

The Gold-Legged Frog

Khamsing Srinawk was born in Thailand in 1930. His family were buffalo farmers, but supported his education into secondary school. He studied economics at Thammasat University and journalism at Chulalongkorn University. He is best known for his short stories, detailing the lives of rural Thai villagers and the social problems they face. In 1992 he was recognised as a 'National Artist of Literature in Thailand'.

The sun blazed as if determined to burn every living thing in the broad fields to a crisp. Now and again the tall, straight, isolated *sabang* and shorea trees let go of some of their dirty yellow leaves. He sat exhausted against a tree trunk, his dark blue shirt wet with sweat. The expanse round him expressed total dryness. He stared at the tufts of dull grass and bits of straw spinning in a column to the sky. The whirlwind sucked brown earth up into the air casting a dark pall over everything. He recalled the old people had told him this was the portent of drought, want, disaster, and death, and he was afraid. He was now anxious to get home; he could already see the tips of the bamboo thickets surrounding the house far ahead like blades of grass. But he hesitated. A moment before reaching the shade of the tree he felt his ears buzz and his eyes blur and knew it meant giddiness and sunstroke. He looked at the soles of his feet blistered from the burning sandy ground and became indescribably angry – angry at the weather capable of such endless torture. In the morning the cold had pierced his bones, but now it was so hot he felt his head would break into pieces. As he recalled the biting cold of the morning, he thought again of his little son.

That very morning he and two of his small children went out into the dry paddy fields near the house to look for frogs for the morning meal. The air was chilly. The two children on either side of him shivered as they stopped to look for frogs hiding in the cracks of the parched earth. Each time they saw two bright eyes in a deep crack,

25 they would shout, 'Pa, here's another one. Pa, this crack has two.
Gold-legged ones! Hurry, Pa.'

He had hopped from place to place as the voices called him,
prying up the dry clods with his hoe. He caught some of the frogs
immediately, but a few jumped away as soon as he began digging. It
30 was the children's job to give chase and pounce on them. Some they
got. Some jumped into other fissures, obliging him to pry up a new
cake of earth. Besides the frog, if his luck were good, he would
unearth a land snail or razor clam waiting for the rains. He would
take these as well.

35 The air had started to warm and already he had had enough frogs
to eat with the morning rice. The sound of drumming, the village
chief's call for a meeting, had sounded faintly from the village. Vague
anger again spilled over as his thoughts returned to that moment. If
only he had gone home then, the poor child would be all right now.
40 It was really the last crack. As soon as he had poked it, the ground
broke apart. A fully-grown gold-legged frog as big as a thumb leaped
past the older child. The younger raced after it for about twelve yards
when it dodged into a deep hoofprint of a water buffalo. The child
groped for it. And then he was shocked almost senseless by the
45 trembling cry of his boy, 'Pa, a snake, a snake bit my hand.'

A cobra spread its hood, hissing. When finally able to act, the
father with all his strength had slammed the handle of his hoe three
times down onto the back of the serpent, leaving its tail twitching. He
carried his child and the basket of frogs home without forgetting to
50 tell the other to drag the snake along as well.

On the way back his son had cried softly and moaned, beating his
chest with his fists and complaining he could not breathe. At home,
the father summoned all the faith healers and herbalists whose names
he could think of and the turmoil began.

55 'Chop up a frog and put it on the wound,' a neighbor called out.

When another shouted, 'Give him the toasted liver of the snake to
eat,' he hurriedly slit open the snake to look for the liver while his
wife sat by crying. The later it got, the bigger the crowd grew. On
hearing the news, all the neighbors attending the village chief's
60 meeting joined the others. One of them told him he had to go to the

district office in town that very day because the village chief told them the government was going to hand out money to those with five or more children, and he was one who had just five. It was a new shock.

65 'Can't you see my boy's gasping out his life? How can I *go*?' he cried resentfully.

'What difference will it make? You've called in a lot of doctors, all of them expert.'

'Go, you fool. It's two hundred baht they're giving. You've never had that much in your whole life. Two hundred!'

70 'Pardon my saying it,' another added, 'but if something should happen and the boy dies, you'd be out, that's all.'

'I won't go,' he yelled. 'My kid can't breathe and you tell me to go. Why can't they hand it out some other day? It's true I've never had two hundred baht since I was born, but I'm not going. I am not

75 going.'

'Jail,' another interjected. 'If you don't go, you simply go to jail. Whoever disobeyed the authorities? If they decide to give, you have to take. If not, jail.'

The word 'jail' repeated like that unnerved him, but still he

80 resisted.

'Whatever it is, I said I'm not going. I don't want it. How can I leave the kid when he's dying?' He raised his voice. 'No, I won't go.'

'You go. Don't go against the government. We're subjects.' He turned to find the village chief standing grimly at his side.

85 'If I don't go, will it really be jail?' he asked in a voice suddenly become hoarse.

'For sure,' the village chief replied sternly. 'Maybe for life.'

That did it. In a daze, he asked the faith healers and neighbors to take care of his son and left the house.

90 He reached the district office almost at eleven and found some of his neighbors who had also come for the money already sitting in a group. They told him to address the old deputy district officer which he did.

'I am Mr Nak Na-ngam, sir. I have come for the money, the many-

95 children money.'

The deputy district officer raised his fat face to stare at him for a moment, then spoke heavily. 'Idiot, don't you have eyes to see people are working. Get out! Get out and wait outside.'

'But, sir, my boy is dying . . .' However he cut himself short when
100 he thought perhaps if the official suspected that his child might be dead there would be trouble. The deputy officer looked down at his paper and went on scribbling. Nak dejectedly joined the group outside. 'All you do is suffer if you're born a rice farmer and a subject,' he thought. 'You're poor and helpless, your mouth gets
105 stained from eating roots when the rice has run out, you're at the end of your tether and you turn to the authorities only to be put down.'

The official continued to write as if there were no peasants waiting anxiously. A few minutes after twelve, he strode from the office but had the kindness to say a few words. 'It's noon already. Time for a
110 break. Come back at one o'clock for it.'

Nak and his neighbors sat there waiting until one o'clock. The taciturn deputy on returning called them all to sit on the floor near him. He began by asking each of them why they had so many children. The awkward replies of the peasants brought guffaws from
115 the other officials who turned to listen to the embarrassed answers. At last his turn came.

'Who is Mr Nak Na-ngam?'

'I am sir,' he responded with humility.

'And now, why do we have such a lot of children?'
120 Several people tittered.

'Oh, when you're poor, sir,' he burst out, his exasperation uncontrollable.

'What the hell's it got to do with being poor?' the deputy officer questioned in a voice that showed disappointment with the answer.
125 'We're awful poor and no money to buy a blanket. So no matter how bad the smell is always, I gotta use my wife for a blanket and the kids just keep comin'.'

Instead of laughter, dead silence, finally broken by the dry voice of the blank-faced deputy, 'Bah! This joker uses his wife for a blanket.'
130 The wind gusted again. The *sabang* and shorea trees threw off another lot of leaves. The spears of sunlight still dazzled him. The

whirlwind still hummed in the middle of the empty rice field ahead. Nak left the shade of the tall tree and headed through the flaming afternoon sunshine towards his village.

135 'Hey, Nak . . .' The voice came from a group of neighbors passing in the opposite direction. Another topped it.

'You sure are lucky.' The words raised his spirits. He smiled a little before repeating expectantly, 'How am I lucky – in what way?'

'The two hundred baht. You got it, didn't you?'

140 'I got it. It's right here.' He patted his pocket.

'What luck! You sure have good luck, Nak. One more day and you'd have been out two hundred baht.'

Amy Tan

USA

Two Kinds

Amy Tan was born in 1952 in Oakland, California. She grew up in the San Francisco Bay area, and received her master's degree in Linguistics from San Jose State University. In 1989 she won The National Book Award and the L.A. Times Book Award for her first novel, *The Joy Luck Club*. Her characters are constantly searching for a balance between their Chinese heritage and their American lifestyle.

My mother believed you could be anything you wanted to be in America. You could open a restaurant. You could work for the government and get good retirement. You could buy a house with almost no money down. You could become rich. You
5 could become instantly famous.

'Of course you can be prodigy, too,' my mother told me when I was nine. 'You can be best anything. What does Auntie Lindo know? Her daughter, she is only best tricky.'

America was where all my mother's hopes lay. She had come here
10 in 1949 after losing everything in China: her mother and father, her family home, her first husband, and two daughters, twin baby girls. But she never looked back with regret. There were so many ways for things to get better.

We didn't immediately pick the right kind of prodigy. At first my
15 mother thought I could be a Chinese Shirley Temple. We'd watch Shirley's old movies on TV as though they were training films. My mother would poke my arm and say, '*Ni kan*' – You watch. And I would see Shirley tapping her feet, or singing a sailor song, or pursing her lips into a very round O while saying, 'Oh my goodness.'
20 '*Ni kan*,' said my mother as Shirley's eyes flooded with tears. 'You already know how. Don't need talent for crying!'

Soon after my mother got this idea about Shirley Temple, she took me to a beauty training school in the Mission district and put me in

the hands of a student who could barely hold the scissors without
shaking. Instead of getting big fat curls, I emerged with an uneven
mass of crinkly black fuzz. My mother dragged me off to the
bathroom and tried to wet down my hair.

'You look like Negro Chinese,' she lamented, as if I had done this
on purpose.

The instructor of the beauty training school had to lop off these
soggy clumps to make my hair even again. 'Peter Pan is very popular
these days,' the instructor assured my mother. I now had hair the
length of a boy's, with straight-across bangs that hung at a slant two
inches above my eyebrows. I liked the haircut and it made me
actually look forward to my future fame.

In fact, in the beginning, I was just as excited as my mother,
maybe even more so. I pictured this prodigy part of me as many
different images, trying each one on for size. I was a dainty ballerina
girl standing by the curtains, waiting to hear the right music that
would send me floating on my tiptoes. I was like the Christ child
lifted out of the straw manger, crying with holy indignity. I was
Cinderella stepping from her pumpkin carriage with sparkly cartoon
music filling the air.

In all of my imaginings, I was filled with a sense that I would soon
become *perfect*. My mother and father would adore me. I would be
beyond reproach. I would never feel the need to sulk for anything.

But sometimes the prodigy in me became impatient. 'If you don't
hurry up and get me out of here, I'm disappearing for good,' it
warned. 'And then you'll always be nothing.'

Every night after dinner, my mother and I would sit at the Formica
kitchen table. She would present new tests, taking her examples from
stories of amazing children she had read in *Ripley's Believe It or Not*,
or *Good Housekeeping*, *Reader's Digest*, and a dozen other magazines
she kept in a pile in our bathroom. My mother got these magazines
from people whose houses she cleaned. And since she cleaned many
houses each week, we had a great assortment. She would look
through them all, searching for stories about remarkable children.

The first night she brought out a story about a three-year-old boy

who knew the capitals of all the states and even most of the
60   European countries. A teacher was quoted as saying the little boy
could also pronounce the names of the foreign cities correctly.

'What's the capital of Finland?' my mother asked me, looking at the
magazine story.

All I knew was the capital of California, because Sacramento was
65   the name of the street we lived on in Chinatown. 'Nairobi!' I guessed,
saying the most foreign word I could think of. She checked to see if
that was possibly one way to pronounce 'Helsinki' before showing me
the answer.

The tests got harder – multiplying numbers in my head, finding the
70   queen of hearts in a deck of cards, trying to stand on my head
without using my hands, predicting the daily temperatures in Los
Angeles, New York, and London.

One night I had to look at a page from the Bible for three minutes
and then report everything I could remember. 'Now Jehoshaphat had
75   riches and honor in abundance and . . . that's all I remember, Ma,' I
said.

And after seeing my mother's disappointed face once again,
something inside of me began to die. I hated the tests, the raised
hopes and failed expectations. Before going to bed that night, I
80   looked in the mirror above the bathroom sink and when I saw only
my face staring back – and that it would always be this ordinary face
– I began to cry. Such a sad, ugly girl! I made high-pitched noises like
a crazed animal, trying to scratch out the face in the mirror.

And then I saw what seemed to be the prodigy side of me –
85   because I had never seen that face before. I looked at my reflection,
blinking so I could see more clearly. The girl staring back at me was
angry, powerful. This girl and I were the same. I had new thoughts,
willful thoughts, or rather thoughts filled with lots of won'ts. I won't
let her change me, I promised myself. I won't be what I'm not.

90   So now on nights when my mother presented her tests, I
performed listlessly, my head propped on one arm. I pretended to be
bored. And I was. I got so bored I started counting the bellows of the
foghorns out on the bay while my mother drilled me in other areas.
The sound was comforting and reminded me of the cow jumping over

95   the moon. And the next day, I played a game with myself, seeing if
my mother would give up on me before eight bellows. After a while I
usually counted only one, maybe two bellows at most. At last she was
beginning to give up hope.

Two or three months had gone by without any mention of my being
100 a prodigy again. And then one day my mother was watching *The Ed
Sullivan Show* on TV. The TV was old and the sound kept shorting
out. Every time my mother got halfway up from the sofa to adjust the
set, the sound would go back on and Ed would be talking. As soon as
she sat down, Ed would go silent again. She got up, the TV broke
105 into loud piano music. She sat down. Silence. Up and down, back
and forth, quiet and loud. It was like a stiff embraceless dance
between her and the TV set. Finally she stood by the set with her
hand on the sound dial.
    She seemed entranced by the music, a little frenzied piano piece
110 with this mesmerizing quality, sort of quick passages and then teasing
lilting ones before it returned to the quick playful parts.
    '*Ni kan*,' my mother said, calling me over with hurried hand
gestures, 'Look here.'
    I could see why my mother was fascinated by the music. It was
115 being pounded out by a little Chinese girl, about nine years old, with
a Peter Pan haircut. The girl had the sauciness of a Shirley Temple.
She was proudly modest like a proper Chinese child. And she also did
this fancy sweep of a curtsy, so that the fluffy skirt of her white dress
cascaded slowly to the floor like the petals of a large carnation.
120   In spite of these warning signs, I wasn't worried. Our family had
no piano and we couldn't afford to buy one, let alone reams of sheet
music and piano lessons. So I could be generous in my comments
when my mother bad-mouthed the little girl on TV.
    'Play note right, but doesn't sound good! No singing sound,'
125 complained my mother.
    'What are you picking on her for?' I said carelessly. 'She's pretty
good. Maybe she's not the best, but she's trying hard.' I knew almost
immediately I would be sorry I said that.
    'Just like you,' she said. 'Not the best. Because you not trying.' She

130 gave a little huff as she let go of the sound dial and sat down on the sofa.

The little Chinese girl sat down also to play an encore of 'Anitra's Dance' by Grieg. I remember the song, because later on I had to learn how to play it.

135 Three days after watching *The Ed Sullivan Show*, my mother told me what my schedule would be for piano lessons and piano practice. She had talked to Mr Chong, who lived on the first floor of our apartment building. Mr Chong was a retired piano teacher and my mother had traded housecleaning services for weekly lessons and a piano for me
140 to practice on every day, two hours a day, from four until six.

When my mother told me this, I felt as though I had been sent to hell. I whined and then kicked my foot a little when I couldn't stand it anymore.

'Why don't you like me the way I am? I'm *not* a genius! I can't play
145 the piano. And even if I could, I wouldn't go on TV if you paid me a million dollars!' I cried.

My mother slapped me. 'Who ask you be genius?' she shouted. 'Only ask you be your best. For you sake. You think I want you be genius? Hnnh! What for! Who ask you!'
150 'So ungrateful,' I heard her mutter in Chinese. 'If she had as much talent as she has temper, she would be famous now.'

Mr Chong, whom I secretly nicknamed Old Chong, was very strange, always tapping his fingers to the silent music of an invisible orchestra. He looked ancient in my eyes. He had lost most of the hair
155 on top of his head and he wore thick glasses and had eyes that always looked tired and sleepy. But he must have been younger than I thought, since he lived with his mother and was not yet married.

I met Old Lady Chong once and that was enough. She had this peculiar smell like a baby that had done something in its pants. And
160 her fingers felt like a dead person's, like an old peach I once found in the back of the refrigerator; the skin just slid off the meat when I picked it up.

I soon found out why Old Chong had retired from teaching piano. He was deaf. 'Like Beethoven!' he shouted to me. 'We're both

165 listening only in our head!' And he would start to conduct his frantic silent sonatas.

Our lessons went like this. He would open the book and point to different things, explaining their purpose: 'Key! Treble! Bass! No sharps or flats! So this is C major! Listen now and play after me!'

170 And then he would play the C scale a few times, a simple chord, and then, as if inspired by an old, unreachable itch, he gradually added more notes and running trills and a pounding bass until the music was really something quite grand.

I would play after him, the simple scale, the simple chord, and
175 then I just played some nonsense that sounded like a cat running up and down on top of garbage cans. Old Chong smiled and applauded and then said, 'Very good! But now you must learn to keep time!'

So that's how I discovered that Old Chong's eyes were too slow to keep up with the wrong notes I was playing. He went through the
180 motions in half-time. To help me keep rhythm, he stood behind me, pushing down on my right shoulder for every beat. He balanced pennies on top of my wrists so I would keep them still as I slowly played scales and arpeggios. He had me curve my hand around an apple and keep that shape when playing chords. He marched stiffly
185 to show me how to make each finger dance up and down, staccato like an obedient little soldier.

He taught me all these things, and that was how I also learned I could be lazy and get away with mistakes, lots of mistakes. If I hit the wrong notes because I hadn't practiced enough, I never corrected
190 myself. I just kept playing in rhythm. And Old Chong kept conducting his own private reverie.

So maybe I never really gave myself a fair chance. I did pick up the basics pretty quickly, and I might have become a good pianist at that young age. But I was so determined not to try, not to be anybody
195 different that I learned to play only the most ear-splitting preludes, the most discordant hymns.

Over the next year, I practiced like this, dutifully in my own way. And then one day I heard my mother and her friend Lindo Jong both talking in a loud bragging tone of voice so others could hear. It was
200 after church, and I was leaning against the brick wall wearing a dress

with stiff white petticoats. Auntie Lindo's daughter, Waverly, who was about my age, was standing farther down the wall about five feet away. We had grown up together and shared all the closeness of two sisters squabbling over crayons and dolls. In other words, for the most
205 part, we hated each other. I thought she was snotty. Waverly Jong had gained a certain amount of fame as 'Chinatown's Littlest Chinese Chess Champion.'

'She bring home too many trophy,' lamented Auntie Lindo that Sunday. 'All day she play chess. All day I have no time do nothing but
210 dust off her winnings.' She threw a scolding look at Waverly, who pretended not to see her.

'You lucky you don't have this problem,' said Auntie Lindo with a sigh to my mother.

And my mother squared her shoulders and bragged: 'Our problem
215 worser than yours. If we ask Jing-mei wash dish, she hear nothing but music. It's like you can't stop this natural talent.'

And right then, I was determined to put a stop to her foolish pride.

A few weeks later, Old Chong and my mother conspired to have me play in a talent show which would be held in the church hall. By
220 then, my parents had saved up enough to buy me a secondhand piano, a black Wurlitzer spinet with a scarred bench. It was the showpiece of our living room.

For the talent show, I was to play a piece called 'Pleading Child' from Schumann's *Scenes from Childhood*. It was a simple, moody
225 piece that sounded more difficult than it was. I was supposed to memorize the whole thing, playing the repeat parts twice to make the piece sound longer. But I dawdled over it, playing a few bars and then cheating, looking up to see what notes followed. I never really listened to what I was playing. I daydreamed about being somewhere
230 else, about being someone else.

The part I liked to practice best was the fancy curtsy: right foot out, touch the rose on the carpet with a pointed foot, sweep to the side, left leg bends, look up and smile.

My parents invited all the couples from the Joy Luck Club to
235 witness my debut. Auntie Lindo and Uncle Tin were there. Waverly

and her two older brothers had also come. The first two rows were
filled with children both younger and older than I was. The littlest
ones got to go first. They recited simple nursery rhymes, squawked
out tunes on miniature violins, twirled Hula Hoops, pranced in pink
240 ballet tutus, and when they bowed or curtsied, the audience would
sigh in unison, 'Awww,' and then clap enthusiastically.

When my turn came, I was very confident. I remember my childish
excitement. It was as if I knew, without a doubt, that the prodigy side
of me really did exist. I had no fear whatsoever, no nervousness. I
245 remember thinking to myself, This is it! This is it! I looked out over
the audience, at my mother's blank face, my father's yawn, Auntie
Lindo's stiff-lipped smile, Waverly's sulky expression. I had on a white
dress layered with sheets of lace, and a pink bow in my Peter Pan
haircut. As I sat down I envisioned people jumping to their feet and
250 Ed Sullivan rushing up to introduce me to everyone on TV.

And I started to play. It was so beautiful. I was so caught up in
how lovely I looked that at first I didn't worry how I would sound. So
it was a surprise to me when I hit the first wrong note and I realized
something didn't sound quite right. And then I hit another and
255 another followed that. A chill started at the top of my head and began
to trickle down. Yet I couldn't stop playing, as though my hands were
bewitched. I kept thinking my fingers would adjust themselves back,
like a train switching to the right track. I played this strange jumble
through two repeats, the sour notes staying with me all the way to the
260 end.

When I stood up, I discovered my legs were shaking. Maybe I had
just been nervous and the audience, like Old Chong, had seen me go
through the right motions and had not heard anything wrong at all. I
swept my right foot out, went down on my knee, looked up and
265 smiled. The room was quiet, except for Old Chong, who was beaming
and shouting, 'Bravo! Bravo! Well done!' But then I saw my mother's
face, her stricken face. The audience clapped weakly, and as I walked
back to my chair, with my whole face quivering as I tried not to cry, I
heard a little boy whisper loudly to his mother, 'That was awful,' and
270 the mother whispered back, 'Well, she certainly tried.'

And now I realized how many people were in the audience, the whole world it seemed. I was aware of eyes burning into my back. I felt the shame of my mother and father as they sat stiffly throughout the rest of the show.

275 We could have escaped during intermission. Pride and some strange sense of honor must have anchored my parents to their chairs. And so we watched it all: the eighteen-year-old boy with a fake mustache who did a magic show and juggled flaming hoops while riding a unicycle. The breasted girl with white makeup who sang
280 from *Madama Butterfly* and got honorable mention. And the eleven-year-old boy who won first prize playing a tricky violin song that sounded like a busy bee.

After the show, the Hsus, the Jongs, and the St Clairs from the Joy Luck Club came up to my mother and father.

285 'Lots of talented kids,' Auntie Lindo said vaguely, smiling broadly.

'That was somethin' else,' said my father, and I wondered if he was referring to me in a humorous way, or whether he even remembered what I had done.

Waverly looked at me and shrugged her shoulders. 'You aren't a
290 genius like me,' she said matter-of-factly. And if I hadn't felt so bad, I would have pulled her braids and punched her stomach.

But my mother's expression was what devastated me: a quiet, blank look that said she had lost everything. I felt the same way, and it seemed as if everybody were now coming up, like gawkers at the
295 scene of an accident, to see what parts were actually missing. When we got on the bus to go home, my father was humming the busy-bee tune and my mother was silent. I kept thinking she wanted to wait until we got home before shouting at me. But when my father unlocked the door to our apartment, my mother walked in and then
300 went to the back, into the bedroom. No accusations. No blame. And in a way, I felt disappointed. I had been waiting for her to start shouting, so I could shout back and cry and blame her for all my misery.

I assumed my talent-show fiasco meant I never had to play the piano
305 again. But two days later, after school, my mother came out of the kitchen and saw me watching TV.

'Four o'clock,' she reminded me as if it were any other day. I was stunned, as though she were asking me to go through the talent-show torture again. I wedged myself more tightly in front of the TV.

310 'Turn off TV,' she called from the kitchen five minutes later.

I didn't budge. And then I decided. I didn't have to do what my mother said anymore. I wasn't her slave. This wasn't China. I had listened to her before and look what happened. She was the stupid one.

315 She came out from the kitchen and stood in the arched entryway of the living room. 'Four o'clock,' she said once again, louder.

'I'm not going to play anymore,' I said nonchalantly. 'Why should I? I'm not a genius.'

She walked over and stood in front of the TV. I saw her chest was

320 heaving up and down in an angry way.

'No!' I said, and I now felt stronger, as if my true self had finally emerged. So this was what had been inside me all along.

'No! I won't!' I screamed.

She yanked me by the arm, pulled me off the floor, snapped off

325 the TV. She was frighteningly strong, half pulling, half carrying me toward the piano as I kicked the throw rugs under my feet. She lifted me up and onto the hard bench. I was sobbing by now, looking at her bitterly. Her chest was heaving even more and her mouth was open, smiling crazily as if she were pleased I was crying.

330 'You want me to be someone that I'm not!' I sobbed. 'I'll never be the kind of daughter you want me to be!'

'Only two kinds of daughters,' she shouted in Chinese. 'Those who are obedient and those who follow their own mind! Only one kind of daughter can live in this house. Obedient daughter!'

335 'Then I wish I wasn't your daughter. I wish you weren't my mother,' I shouted. As I said these things I got scared. It felt like worms and toads and slimy things crawling out of my chest, but it also felt good, as if this awful side of me had surfaced, at last.

'Too late change this,' said my mother shrilly.

340 And I could sense her anger rising to its breaking point. I wanted to see it spill over. And that's when I remembered the babies she had lost in China, the ones we never talked about. 'Then I wish I'd never

been born!' I shouted. 'I wish I were dead! Like them.'

345 It was as if I had said the magic words. Alakazam! – and her face went blank, her mouth closed, her arms went slack, and she backed out of the room, stunned, as if she were blowing away like a small brown leaf, thin, brittle, lifeless.

It was not the only disappointment my mother felt in me. In the years that followed, I failed her so many times, each time asserting my own
350 will, my right to fall short of expectations. I didn't get straight As. I didn't become class president. I didn't get into Stanford. I dropped out of college.

For unlike my mother, I did not believe I could be anything I wanted to be. I could only be me.

355 And for all those years, we never talked about the disaster at the recital or my terrible accusations afterward at the piano bench. All that remained unchecked, like a betrayal that was now unspeakable. So I never found a way to ask her why she had hoped for something so large that failure was inevitable.

360 And even worse, I never asked her what frightened me the most: Why had she given up hope?

For after our struggle at the piano, she never mentioned my playing again. The lessons stopped. The lid to the piano was closed, shutting out the dust, my misery, and her dreams.

365 So she surprised me. A few years ago, she offered to give me the piano, for my thirtieth birthday. I had not played in all those years. I saw the offer as a sign of forgiveness, a tremendous burden removed.

'Are you sure?' I asked shyly. 'I mean, won't you and Dad miss it?'

'No, this your piano,' she said firmly. 'Always your piano. You only
370 one can play.'

'Well, I probably can't play anymore,' I said. 'It's been years.'

'You pick up fast,' said my mother, as if she knew this was certain. 'You have natural talent. You could been genius if you want to.'

'No I couldn't.'

375 'You just not trying,' said my mother. And she was neither angry nor sad. She said it as if to announce a fact that could never be disproved. 'Take it,' she said.

But I didn't at first. It was enough that she had offered it to me. And after that, every time I saw it in my parents' living room, standing
380 in front of the bay windows, it made me feel proud, as if it were a shiny trophy I had won back.

Last week I sent a tuner over to my parents' apartment and had the piano reconditioned, for purely sentimental reasons. My mother had died a few months before and I had been getting things in order for
385 my father, a little bit at a time. I put the jewelry in special silk pouches. The sweaters she had knitted in yellow, pink, bright orange – all the colors I hated – I put those in moth-proof boxes. I found some old Chinese silk dresses, the kind with little slits up the sides. I rubbed the old silk against my skin, then wrapped them in tissue and
390 decided to take them home with me.

After I had the piano tuned, I opened the lid and touched the keys. It sounded even richer than I remembered. Really, it was a very good piano. Inside the bench were the same exercise notes with handwritten scales, the same secondhand music books with their
395 covers held together with yellow tape.

I opened up the Schumann book to the dark little piece I had played at the recital. It was on the left-hand side of the page, 'Pleading Child.' It looked more difficult than I remembered. I played a few bars, surprised at how easily the notes came back to me.

400 And for the first time, or so it seemed, I noticed the piece on the right-hand side. It was called 'Perfectly Contented.' I tried to play this one as well. It had a lighter melody but the same flowing rhythm and turned out to be quite easy. 'Pleading Child' was shorter but slower; 'Perfectly Contented' was longer, but faster. And after I played them
405 both a few times, I realized they were two halves of the same song.

Feng Ji-cai

CHINA

The Tall Woman and Her Short Husband

**Feng Ji-cai was born in China in 1942 and brought up in Tianjin. He
began writing in his spare time but by profession he was a teacher of
traditional Chinese painting. His first novel, *The Boxer*, was highly
acclaimed and Ji-cai began writing full time after its publication. He
won national awards for his short story 'The Figure-Carved Pipe' and his
novel *Ah!*. The following story is set in China at a time of great political
change and upheaval, sometimes known as the 'Cultural Revolution'.**

1

Say you have a small tree in your yard and are used to its
smooth trunk. If one day it turns twisted and gnarled it strikes
you as awkward. As time goes by, however, you grow to like it,
as if that was how this tree should always have been. Were it
suddenly to straighten out again you would feel indescribably put out.
A trunk as dull and boring as a stick! In fact it would simply have
reverted to its original form, so why should you worry?

Is this force of habit? Well, don't underestimate 'habit'. It runs
through everything done under the sun. It is not a law to be strictly
observed, yet flouting it is simply asking for trouble. Don't complain
though if it proves so binding that sometimes, unconsciously, you
conform to it. For instance, do you presume to throw your weight
about before your superiors? Do you air your views recklessly in front
of your seniors? When a group photograph is taken, can you shove
celebrities aside to stand swaggering and chortling in the middle? You
can't, of course you can't. Or again, would you choose a wife ten
years older than you, heftier than you or a head taller than you? Don't
be in a rush to answer. Here's an instance of such a couple.

2

She was seventeen centimetres taller than he.

One point seven five metres in height, she towered above most of her sex like a crane over chickens. Her husband, a bare 1.58 metres, had been nicknamed Shorty at college. He came up to her earlobes but actually looked two heads shorter.

And take their appearances. She seemed dried up and scrawny with a face like an unvarnished ping-pong bat. Her features would pass, but they were small and insignificant as if carved in shallow relief. She was flat-chested, had a ramrod back and buttocks as scraggy as a scrubbing board. Her husband on the other hand seemed a rubber rolypoly: well-fleshed, solid and radiant. Everything about him – his calves, insteps, lips, nose and fingers – were like pudgy little meatballs. He had soft skin and a fine complexion shining with excess fat and ruddy because of all the red blood in his veins. His eyes were like two high-voltage little light bulbs, while his wife's were like glazed marbles. The two of them just did not match, and formed a marked contrast. But they were inseparable.

One day some of their neighbours were having a family reunion. After drinking his fill the grandfather put a tall, thin empty wine bottle on the table next to a squat tin of pork.

'Who do these remind you of?' he asked. Before anyone could guess he gave the answer. 'That tall woman downstairs and that short husband of hers.'

Everyone burst out laughing and went on laughing through the meal.

What had brought such a pair together?

This was a mystery to the dozens of households living in Unity Mansions. Ever since this couple moved in, the old residents had eyed them curiously. Some registered a question mark in their minds, while others put their curiosity into words. Tongues started wagging, especially in wet weather when the two of them went out and it was always Mrs Tall who held the umbrella. If anything dropped to the ground, though, it was simpler for Mr Short to pick it up. Some old ladies at a loose end would gesticulate, finding this comic, and splutter with laughter. This set a bad example for the children who

would burst out laughing at the sight of the pair and hoot, 'Long
55 carrying-pole; big, low stool!' The husband and wife pretended not to
hear and kept their tempers, paying no attention. Maybe for this
reason their relations with their neighbours remained rather cool. The
few less officious ones simply nodded a greeting when they met. This
made it hard for those really intrigued by them to find out more about
60 them. For instance, how did they hit it off? Why had they married?
Which gave way to the other? They could only speculate.

This was an old-fashioned block of flats with large sunny rooms
and wide, dark corridors. It stood in a big courtyard with a small
gatehouse. The man who lived there was a tailor, a decent fellow. His
65 wife, who brimmed over with energy, liked to call on her neighbours
and gossip. Most of all she liked to ferret out their secrets. She knew
exactly how husbands and wives got on, why sisters-in-law
quarrelled, who was lazy, who hard-working, and how much
everyone earned. If she was unclear about anything she would leave
70 no stone unturned to get at the truth. The thirst for knowledge makes
even the ignorant wise. In this respect she was outstanding. She
analysed conversations, watched expressions, and could even tell
what people were secretly thinking. Simply by using her nose, she
knew which household was eating meat or fish, and from that could
75 deduce their income. For some reason or other, ever since the sixties
each housing estate had chosen someone like this as a
'neighbourhood activist', giving legal status to these nosey-parkers so
that their officiousness could have full play. It seems the Creator will
never waste any talent.

80 Though the tailor's wife was indefatigable she failed to discover
how this incongruous couple who passed daily before her eyes had
come to marry. She found this most frustrating; it posed a formidable
challenge. On the basis of her experience, however, and by racking
her brains she finally came up with a plausible explanation: either
85 husband or wife must have some physiological deficiency. Otherwise
no one would marry someone a whole head taller or shorter. Her
grounds for this reasoning were that after three years of marriage they
still had no children. The residents of Unity Mansions were all
convinced by this brilliant hypothesis.

90   But facts are merciless. The tailor's wife was debunked and lost
      face when Mrs Tall appeared in the family way. Her womb could be
      seen swelling from day to day, for being relatively far from the
      ground it was all too evident. Regardless of their amazement,
      misgivings or embarrassment, she gave birth to a fine baby. When the
95   sun was hot or it rained and the couple went out, Mrs Tall would
      carry the baby while Mr Short held the umbrella. He plodded along
      comically on his plump legs, the umbrella held high, keeping just
      behind his wife. And the neighbours remained as intrigued as at the
      start by this ill-assorted, inseparable couple. They went on making
100   plausible conjectures, but could find no confirmation for any of them.
      The tailor's wife said, 'They must have something to hide, those
      two. Why else should they keep to themselves? Well, it's bound to
      come to light some day, just wait and see.'
      One evening, sure enough, she heard the sound of breaking glass
105   in their flat. On the pretext of collecting money for sweeping the yard
      she rushed to knock on their door, sure that their long hidden feud
      had come to a head and avid to watch the confrontation between
      them. The door opened. Mrs Tall asked her in with a smile. Mr Short
      was smiling too at a smashed plate on the floor – that was all the
110   tailor's wife saw. She hastily collected the money and left to puzzle
      over what had happened. A plate had been smashed, yet instead of
      quarrelling they had treated it as a joke. How very strange!
      Later the tailor's wife became the residents' representative for
      Unity Mansions. When she helped the police check up on living
115   permits, she at last found the answer to this puzzle. A reliable and
      irrefutable answer. The tall woman and her short husband both
      worked in the Research Institute of the Ministry of Chemical Industry.
      He was chief engineer, with a salary of over 180 yuan! She was an
      ordinary laboratory technician earning less than sixty yuan, and her
120   father was a hard-working low-paid postman. So that explained why
      she had married a man so much shorter. For status, money and an
      easy life. Right! The tailor's wife lost no time in passing on this
      priceless information to all the bored old ladies in Unity Mansions.
      Judging others by themselves, they believed her. At last this riddle
125   was solved. They saw the light. Rich Mr Short was congenitally

deficient while poor Mrs Tall was a money-grabber on the make. When they discussed the good luck of this tall woman who looked like a horse, they often voiced resentment – especially the tailor's wife.

3

Sometimes good luck turns into bad.

130   In 1966, disaster struck China. Great changes came into the lives of all the residents in Unity Mansions, which was like a microcosm of the whole country. Mr Short as chief engineer was the first to suffer. His flat was raided, his furniture moved out, he was struggled against and confined in his institute. And worse was to come. He was accused of

135   smuggling out the results of his research to write up at home in the evenings, with a view to fleeing the country to join a wealthy relative abroad. This preposterous charge of passing on scientific secrets to foreign capitalists was widely believed. In that period of lunacy people took leave of their senses and cruelly made up groundless accusations

140   in order to find some Hitler in their midst. The institute kept a stranglehold on its chief engineer. He was threatened, beaten up, put under all kinds of pressure; his wife was ordered to hand over that manuscript which no one had ever seen. But all was to no effect. Someone proposed holding a struggle meeting against them both in

145   the courtyard of Unity Mansions. As everyone dreads losing face in front of relatives and friends, this would put more pressure on them. Since all else had failed, it was at least worth trying. Never before had Unity Mansions been the scene of such excitement.

In the afternoon the institute sent people to fix up ropes between

150   two trees in the yard, on which to hang a poster with the name of Mr Short on it – crossed out. Inside and outside the yard they pasted up threatening slogans, and on the wall put eighteen more posters listing the engineer's 'crimes'. As the meeting was to be held after supper, an electrician was sent to fix up four big 500-watt bulbs. By now the

155   tailor's wife, promoted to be the chairman of the neighbourhood's Public Security Committee, was a powerful person, full of self-importance, and much fatter than before. She had been busy all day bossing the other women about, helping to put up slogans and make tea for the revolutionaries from the institute. The wiring for the lights

160 had been fixed up from her gatehouse as if she were celebrating a
wedding!

After supper the tailor's wife assembled all the residents in the
yard, lit up as brilliantly as a sportsground at night. Their shadows,
magnified ten-fold, were thrown on the wall of the building. These
165 shadows stayed stock-still, not even the children daring to play about.
The tailor's wife led a group also wearing red armbands, in those days
most awe-inspiring, to guard the gate and keep outsiders out.
Presently a crowd from the institute, wearing armbands and shouting
slogans, marched in the tall woman and her short husband. He had a
170 placard hung round his neck, she had none. The two of them were
marched in front of the platform, and stood there side by side with
lowered heads.

The tailor's wife darted forward. 'This wretch is too short for the
revolutionary masses at the back to see,' she cried. 'I'll soon fix that.'
175 She dashed into the gatehouse, her fat shoulders heaving, to fetch a
soapbox which she turned upside down. Mr Short standing on this
was the same height as his wife. But at this point little attention was
paid to the relative heights of this couple facing disaster.

The meeting followed the customary procedure. After slogans had
180 been shouted, passionate accusations were made, punctuated by more
slogans. The pressure built up. First Mrs Tall was ordered to come
clean, to produce that 'manuscript'. Questions and denunciations were
fired at her, hysterical screams, angry shouts and threatening growls.
But she simply shook her head gravely and sincerely. What use was
185 sincerity? To believe in her would have made the whole business a
farce.

No matter what bullies sprang forward to shake their fists at her, or
what tricky questions were asked to try to trap her, she simply shook
her head. The members of the institute were at a loss, afraid that if this
190 went on the struggle meeting would fizzle out and end up a fiasco.

The tailor's wife had listened with mounting exasperation. Being
illiterate she took no interest in the 'manuscript' they wanted, and felt
these research workers were too soft-spoken. All of a sudden she ran
to the platform. Raising her right arm with its red armband she pointed
195 accusingly at Mrs Tall.

'Say!' she screeched. 'Why did you marry him?'

The members of the institute were staggered by this unexpected question. What connection had it with their investigation?

200 Mrs Tall was staggered too. This wasn't the sort of question asked these days. She looked up with surprise on her thin face which showed the ravages of the last few months.

'So you don't dare answer, eh?' The tailor's wife raised her voice. 'I'll answer for you! You married this scoundrel, didn't you, for his money? If he hadn't had money who'd want such a short fellow!' She
205 sounded rather smug, as if she alone had seen through Mrs Tall.

Mrs Tall neither nodded nor shook her head. She had seen through the tailor's wife too. Her eyes glinted with derision and contempt.

'All right, you won't admit it. This wretch is done for now, he's a
210 broken reed. Oh, I know what you're thinking.' The tailor's wife slapped her chest and brandished one hand gloatingly. Some other women chimed in.

The members of the institute were flummoxed. A question like this was best ignored. But though these women had strayed far from the
215 subject, they had also livened up the meeting. So the institute members let them take the field. The women yelled:

'How much has he paid you? What has he bought you? What has he bought you? Own up!'

'Two hundred a month isn't enough for you, is it? You have to go
220 abroad!'

'Is Deng Tuo behind you?'

'That day you made a long-distance call to Beijing, were you ringing up the Three Family Village?'

The success of a meeting depends on the enthusiasm worked up.
225 The institute members who had convened this meeting saw that the time was ripe now to shout a few more slogans and conclude it. They then searched Mrs Tall's flat, prising up floorboards and stripping off wallpaper. When they discovered nothing, they marched her husband away, leaving her behind.

230 Mrs Tall stayed in all the next day but went out alone after dark, unaware that though the light in the gatehouse was out the tailor's

wife was watching her from the window. She trailed her out of the gate and past two crossroads till Mrs Tall stopped to knock softly on a gate. The tailor's wife ducked behind a telegraph pole and waited,

235 holding her breath, as if to pounce on a rabbit when it popped out of its burrow.

The gate creaked open. An old woman led out a child.

'All over, is it?' she asked.

Mrs Tall's answer was inaudible.

240 'He's had his supper and a sleep,' the old woman said. 'Take him home quickly now.'

The tailor's wife realised that this was the woman who minded their little boy. Her excitement died down as Mrs Tall turned back to lead her son home. All was silence apart from the sound of their

245 footsteps. The tailor's wife stood motionless behind the telegraph pole till they had gone, then scurried home herself.

The next morning when Mrs Tall led her son out, her eyes were red. No one would speak to her, but they all saw her red, swollen eyes. Those who had denounced her the previous day had a strange feeling

250 of guilt. They turned away so as not to meet her eyes.

4

After the struggle meeting Mr Short was not allowed home again. The tailor's wife, who was in the know, said he had been imprisoned as an active counter-revolutionary. That made Mrs Tall the lowest of the low, naturally unfit to live in a roomy flat. She was forced to change

255 places with the tailor's wife and moved into the little gatehouse. This didn't worry her, as it meant she could avoid the other residents who snubbed her. But they could look through her window and see her all alone there. Where she had sent her son, they didn't know, for he only came home for a few days at a time. Ostracised by all, she

260 looked older than a woman in her thirties.

'Mark my words,' the tailor's wife said, 'she can only keep this up for at most a year. Then if Shorty doesn't get out she'll have to remarry. If I were her I'd get a divorce and remarry. Even if he's let out his name will be mud, and he won't have any money.'

265   A year went by. Mr Short still didn't come back and Mrs Tall kept to herself. In silence she went to work, came back, lit her stove and went out with a big shabby shopping basket. Day after day she did this, the whole year round . . . But one day in autumn Mr Short reappeared – thinly clad, his head shaved, and his whole appearance

270 changed. He seemed to have shrunk and his skin no longer gleamed with health. He went straight to his old flat. Its new master, the honest tailor, directed him to the gatehouse. Mrs Tall was squatting in the doorway chopping firewood. At the sound of his voice she sprang up to stare at him. After two years' separation both were appalled by the

275 change in the other. One was wrinkled, the other haggard; one looked taller than before, the other shorter. After gazing at each other they hastily turned away, and Mrs Tall ran inside. When finally she came out again he had picked up the axe and squatted down to chop firewood, until two big boxes of wood had been chopped into

280 kindling, as if he feared some new disaster might befall them at any moment. After that they were inseparable again, going to work together and coming back together just as before. The neighbours, finding them unchanged, gradually lost interest in them and ignored them.

285   One morning Mrs Tall had an accident. Her husband rushed frantically out and came back with an ambulance to fetch her. For days the gatehouse was empty and dark at night. After three weeks Mr Short returned with a stranger. They were carrying her on a stretcher. She was confined to her room. He went to work as usual,

290 hurrying back at dusk to light the stove and go out with the shopping basket. This was the same basket she had used every day. In his hand it looked even bigger and nearly reached the ground.

     When the weather turned warmer Mrs Tall came out. After so long in bed her face was deathly white, and she swayed from side to side.

295 She held a cane in her right hand and kept her elbow bent in front of her. Her half-paralysed left leg made walking difficult. She had obviously had a stroke. Every morning and every evening Mr Short helped her twice round the yard, painfully and slowly. By hunching up his shoulders he was able to grip her crooked arm in both hands.

300 It was hard for him, but he smiled to encourage her. As she couldn't

raise her left foot, he tied a rope round it and pulled this up when she wanted to take a step forward. This was a pathetic yet impressive sight, and the neighbours were touched by it. Now when they met the couple they nodded cordially to them.

5

305 Mrs Tall's luck had run out: she was not to linger long by the side of the short husband who had loved her so dearly. Death and life were equally cruel to her. Life had struck her down and now death carried her off. Mr Short was left all alone.

But after her death fortune smiled on him again. He was
310 rehabilitated, his confiscated possessions were returned, and he received all his back pay. Only his flat, occupied by the tailor's wife, was not given back to him. The neighbours watched to see what he would do. It was said that some of his colleagues had proposed finding him another wife, but he had declined their offers.

315 'I know the kind of woman he wants,' said the tailor's wife. 'Just leave it to me!'

Having passed her zenith she had become more subdued. Stripped of her power she had to wear a smile. With a photograph of a pretty girl in her pocket she went to the gatehouse to find Mr Short. The girl
320 in the picture was her niece.

She sat in the gatehouse sizing up its furnishing as she proposed this match to rich Mr Short. Smiling all over her face she held forth with gusto until suddenly she realised that he had not said a word, his face was black, and behind him hung a picture of him and Mrs Tall
325 on their wedding day. Then she beat a retreat without venturing to produce the photograph of her niece.

Since then several years have passed. Mr Short is still a widower, but on Sundays he fetches his son home to keep him company. At the sight of his squat, lonely figure, his neighbours recall all that he has
330 been through and have come to understand why he goes on living alone. When it rains and he takes an umbrella to go to work, out of force of habit perhaps he still holds it high. Then they have the strange sensation that there is a big empty space under that umbrella, a vacuum that nothing on earth can fill.

Karl Sealy

The Pieces of Silver

Karl Sealy was born in Barbados in 1932. He was a storywriter, poet and critic. His work has appeared in several anthologies, including *Global Tales*, edited by Beverley Naidoo. He also wrote for Caribbean journals and the magazine *Bim*. The following story tells of a time when the relationship between teachers and pupils was far from what it is today.

When, at five minutes to ten, the bell started to ring, a pall of silence settled over the noisy playfield.

Reluctantly games of cricket and pick-ups were abandoned; climbers came slithering down from the old tamarind tree on the school grounds or dropped quickly from its branches, making
5 haste to clear their mouths of the green, acid fruit they had been enjoying.

The school of four hundred odd boys assembled in ranks across the pebbled playfield, waiting for inspection before they could file into the red-walled school. Some glanced apprehensively at their
10 dusty, naked feet, while others tried feverishly to make their nails and hands presentable.

The teachers came from the schoolroom in a leisurely bunch, laughing and joking in quiet voices as they sauntered towards the boys.

15 The stout, pompous, acting Headmaster came to the window that opened off his platform on to the playfield, still making an unnecessary clangour with his bell, and looked sternly over the assembled rows of scholars. The smaller boys straightened and stiffened under his cold gaze.

20 As the teachers passed slowly along the ranks the boys turned their hands back and forth and grinned to show their teeth. A number of boys who failed to pass the teachers' inspection of health were hauled out of the ranks and ordered in to the acting Head. There were three strokes with his cane of plaited tamarind stalks for unclean

25   hands; four for improperly brushed teeth and six for an uncombed head.

     After the inspection the boys filed quietly into school and to their different classes. When you could have heard a pin drop the schoolmaster rapped out the order: 'Shun!' The entire school of boys

30   flung their hands to their foreheads and chanted: 'Good morning to our teachers.'

     The schoolmaster announced a hymn, and emitting an untrue, faltering note, invited the scholars to take it. The boys rendered a rich improvement of the sound, and when the schoolmaster flung his hand

35   up and stamped his foot they tore full-throatedly into the hymn.

     At the conclusion of the hymn the boys sang, 'Amen,' bringing their hands up to their faces in an attitude of prayer. The schoolmaster submitted a long, impromptu supplication, rambling and ill-worded, at the end of which the boys said 'Amen' once more. Again the

40   schoolmaster ordered: 'Shun!' The boys came to attention, and school was ready to begin.

     But this morning the schoolmaster did not order the school to be seated as was the normal custom after prayers. Instead he fixed the school with his cold eyes and said:

45   'Those who have brought contributions to Mr Megahey's purse will give them to their teachers.'

     Hands delved into pockets, while, in the lower classes, a number of small, moist fists closed still more tightly over the pieces of silver which had been wrapped in paper and pressed carefully into their

50   palms.

     The teachers drew chairs and stools to their respective desks and sat down. Each produced a foolscap sheet on which were recorded the names of those of his class who had contributed to the purse for the retiring Head, Mr Megahey.

55   No commendation seemed due to the donor of threepence. A sixpence was held up between the thumb and forefinger of the receiving teacher and displayed before the class, while the name of the boy who had presented it was repeated some half a dozen times. Still more ado was made of the bestower of a shilling. In addition to

60   being patted on the shoulder and beamed on by his teacher, and

basking in the envy of his class, he was sent up to be thanked by the acting Head who shook his hand heartily and showed the gleaming gold of his teeth, and who, with a grave gesture, bestowed upon him the fag-end of a stick of chalk with the injunction that it be not used
65 about the school.

The receipt of the contributions was over, and the last boy had returned to his seat. On the platform the acting Head cleared his throat for attention and said:

'Those who have contributed to our retiring Head's purse will now
70 sit. Those who have *not* will remain standing.'

When the scuffling tumult of a school of boys taking their seats had subsided, here and there about the schoolroom a scattered few stood with downcast eyes.

The acting Head was a squat jug of a man, fierce-eyed and
75 unsmiling. He now sauntered along the edge of his platform and fixed, one after the other, each of the standing boys with a look of complete scorn. Then, mopping his brow, he ordered those who had brought no gifts to come up and mount the platform where the dozen of them were lined up.

80 Taking a stick of chalk he scrawled an X upon the forehead of each boy, to the huge delight of the rest of the school. When he had imprinted this symbol of shame upon the brow of each unhappy child, he turned to the laughing school, and holding his hand up to check the gusts of merriment, said:

85 'Look! They bear the symbol of ingratitude!'

The cruel laughter went up to the rafters. The schoolmaster permitted it free swell for a few moments before raising his hand once more.

'Ingratitude,' he went on, 'ingratitude, more strong than human
90 hand . . . Come, Clement. You're in the fourth. Step forward and let's hear Mark Antony on ingratitude. Surely our old Head would expire if he knew that in his school he harboured so many thankless Brutuses. Come, Clement, let us hear you recite the piece, and well.'

Clement stepped forward, shabby and barefoot, and with eyes
95 downcast, began to recite the passage in a choked, monotonous tone. Now and again the schoolmaster threatened him with his rod,

exhorting him to speak up. The boy would then raise his voice and quicken his words under the threat of the lash, but soon his voice sank back and the recitation resumed its muttered vein.

100 At last, however, the passage was finished. The acting Headmaster then spent some minutes more making the hapless boys the laughing-stock of their schoolfriends. Only when he thought the school on the verge of becoming unmanageable did he dismiss the tormented boys with the words:

105 'Now go to your places. But bear in mind, every morning, until you show some appreciation for your resigning Headmaster, you shall come up here and stand in shame before the whole school.'

It was dusk, and the Dovecots were taking their one substantial meal of the day.

110 No one could think, looking at their home, that threepenny pieces, or even halfpennies, were to be had there for the asking.

The house was a poor, wretched coop of a room, through the black, water-stained shingles of which you could count a dozen blue glimpses of the sky. The walls of the shack were papered with old

115 newspapers and magazines, discoloured with age and stained and spotted from roof to floor, torn in a score of places, to reveal the rotting, worm-eaten boards beneath. The small room was divided by a threadbare cotton screen depicting seagulls soaring up from a sea of faded blue. In the midst of this drab poverty the free, soaring seagulls,

120 and the once gay pictures of the magazine pages were an unkind comment.

The Dovecots were a family of four: Dave and his wife Maud, Clement and his older sister Evelina.

Clement sat on the sanded floor of the poor sitting-room, his plate of

125 rice between his legs; Evelina lolled over the one battered, depreciated mahogany table, picking at the coarse food with an adolescent discontent; Dave Dovecot, a grizzled, gangling labourer, held his plate in his left hand, while with his right he plied his mouth from a peeling metal spoon; at the propped-open window of the

130 room sat Mrs Dovecot, a long thread of a woman whose bones want

had picked like an eagle. Her plate was resting on her lap, and she scraped and pecked and foraged her food like a scratching hen, while she took stock of the passers-by.

When Clement had finished, he took up his empty plate and, getting to his feet, went and stowed it away in the dark box of a kitchen. Returning, he slumped down beside his mother's chair and rested his head against her bony thigh.

After a time he said:

'Ma, could I have the threepence I's been asking for Mr Megahey?'

'Hmn. Wa' threepence boy? Why in de name of de Lord must poor starving people got to find threepences for Jim Megahey what's got his belly sitting so pretty wi' fat?' parried Mrs Dovecot, though she knew well enough.

'I's told you and told you and told you, Ma. He's resigning and we've all got to take threepence to give him,' explained Clement patiently once more.

'Hmn. Threepence is a lot o' money for us poor folk. Hmn. Go ax your father. See what *he* says.' Clement got to his feet reluctantly and moved slowly over to where his father was sitting, for he knew from experience that, in parting with money, his father was a far harder nut to crack than his mother.

Dave Dovecot utilised the approach of his son by extending his empty plate. Clement took the plate to the kitchen. Then he turned once more to tackle his father.

'Can I have a threepence, Papa?' he shouted in his father's ear, for the old man was pretty nigh stone deaf.

'Eh-eh! What's that about a fence, Clement?'

This time Clement put his mouth completely into his father's ear and shouted until his dark face grew darker.

'Eh-eh! Don't shout at me,' was all he got for his pains. 'Don't you deafen me. What's that the young varmint says, Maud?'

Mrs Dovecot came over, and got him to understand after two or three attempts.

'Three pence, Maudie,' he cackled, 'three pence! Did yo' hear thet, Maud? Did yo' ever hear the like? I'll bet you ain't never did. Three pence! The lad'll have money what I's got to sweat blood for, just to gi to thet Megahey what's got his bread so well buttered off 'pon both sides not to mention the middle. Three pence! Ha ha! . . . oh Maudie . . .' And he broke down once more in helpless laughter.

170 Clement went out and sat under the breadfruit tree that grew before the door, resting his back against the trunk.

Evelina came to him there when the dusk was thick and sat beside him.

There was a close bond of understanding and companionship
175 between these two. Clement leaned against her so that he could feel the cheering warmth of her arms, warm as the still warm ground beneath him. Biting his nails he told her of his morning's shame.

She listened as attentively as a mother, and as she listened, she put her hand around his neck and drew his head gently down upon her
180 young bosom.

When he had finished talking she put her lips down to his harsh curls, and thought for a long time. Then she said, with a little sigh:

'I know what we'll do, Clemmie. 'Member how 'fore I was took from school we big girls used to go out singing at Christmas? Well,
185 we'll play waits. Only tonight there'll be only you and me.'

Clement raised his head and gazed into her face in the starlight.

'Oh, Eve,' he said, 'but it ain't anyways near Christmas.'

'Never you mind,' she said. 'There's still some who'll give us a penny or two. You wait. I'll get our hats and then we'll be off.'

190 She got to her feet and slipped quickly into the house. She returned in a few moments carrying his cap in her hand, her own hat of straw on her head. She settled his cap, then produced a comb.

'When we come to the shop we'll ask for a piece of bread paper,' she said, 'then you'll play the sax while I sing.'

195 They roamed far that night. Evelina's voice rose clear and true to the accompaniment of the paper and comb, long after the moon came up and laid white hands upon the countryside.

At last Evelina said, jingling the coins which they had earned in the pockets of her dress:

200 'Let's make this our last and call it a day.'

The house with which they proposed to round off their tour had a pretentious front of red brick. The greater part of the house was in darkness, but from the street the two children could see a couple sitting in the open veranda.

205   Bravely, Evelina unlatched the street gate and led the way up the steps to the veranda.

   'Good night,' she greeted the pair in the shadows. 'We would like to sing for you.'

   The woman chuckled softly and Evelina could see the white gleam
210 of the man's teeth when he said, 'Sure.'

   The children rendered their song. When they had finished the man got to his feet and approached them, delving in his pocket.

   'Thanks for your singing,' he said kindly. 'It was very nice. May, give us some light for a moment.'

215   The woman got from her chair and, leaning through a window, pressed a light switch.

   And as the light flooded the veranda little Clement was turned to stone, for the tall, greying man foraging the handful of coins was the retiring Headmaster, Mr Megahey.

220   Clement's scrambled retreat after Evelina had made her little curtsy was perhaps unnecessary, since Mr Megahey had his glasses off and he didn't seem to recognise him.

   Out in the road, Evelina let out the laughter that had been welling inside her.

225   'Just think how we never thought of where your old Head might've moved to after he left the Schoolmaster's house,' she laughed. 'But he's gi'n us our biggest taking for the night, anyway. He's gi'n us sixpence.'

   They counted their takings in the middle of the white road in the
230 moonlight. When they had finished, Evelina poured the coins back into her pocket and said:

   'Now I going tell you how we'll fix that brute, Mr Chase.'

   On the following morning the acting Head, Mr Chase, kept his word. Immediately after prayers the boys who had brought no silver
235 were lined up across the platform. They were but eight of them this morning. Two had somehow managed their threepenny pieces, while two or three others had absented themselves. Clement counted the line of boys as he took his place among them.

As Mr Chase eyed their bowed heads in enjoyment, Clement
240   stepped forward, the eight pieces of silver upon his extended palm.

'There are eight,' he told the gaping schoolmaster. 'One for *each*
of us.'

His voice struck through the silent school, clear and thrilling as a
star's light.

Ismith Khan

CARIBBEAN

The Red Ball

**Ismith Khan was born in Trinidad and Tobago in 1925 and is the author
of the classic Caribbean novels, *The Jumbie Bird*, *The Crucifixion* and
The Obeah Man. It was said of *The Obeah Man* that 'Khan's tale of
people living in the slow-moving tropics packs life into every word'.
Khan has also written several short stories. The following story
describes a boy's experiences as he and his family try to adjust to a new
life in the capital city of Trinidad and Tobago, Port of Spain.**

'Aye . . . Thinny Boney! You want to play?'
        One of the boys called out to him, and although he had
heard and knew they were calling him, he kept pulling out
the red petals of the hibiscus flower, tore off their bottom ends and
5   blew into the fine pores of the needle holes at the base until the
petals swelled out into a thin balloon of pink skin which he pierced
with the straight pin which kept his shirt front closed.
        'Match-stick foot! You playin' deaf. You want to play or you don't
want to play?'
10   In his childish way, the boy had understood that if he answered to
any of the names they coined for him, he would have to live with it
forever. For two weeks now, since they moved to Port of Spain, he
had been coming to Woodford Square in the evenings. At first he sat
in the fountain with his long thin legs dangling in the water, the spray
15   falling on his face, and when no one was going past he waded across
the waist-high water to the green and mossy man-sized busts where
there was a giant of a man standing lordly among four half-fish half-
women creatures, a tall trident in his massive arm pointing to the shell
of blue sky. He had touched the strong green veins running down the
20   calves of the man's legs with fear, half expecting the severe lips to
smile, or even curl in anger at him, but the lips stood still in their
severity. He then held his cheek close to the small breast of one of
the smiling women seated back to back at the feet of the standing

man, and she seemed to smile. That was the first time he felt as
though he were back in Tunapuna, before they moved.

'Aye you! What you name? You have a name or you ain't have a
name?'

He looked at the boys through slitted eyes, still seated on the foot-
high cement runner that ran around Woodford Square with tall iron
rails pierced deep into the runner. On previous evenings, when the
city workers were still wending their ways home through the short-cut
square, he had stayed away from its centre and its fountain, catching
the flowers of the yellow and purple poui as they spun sailing
earthwards. He waited like a small animal scenting the wind with his
nostrils until some small gust unhinged a flower and he went racing
below the path it was slowly tracing as it came spinning and dancing
slowly down to earth. During the past week he came and sat on the
runner where the boys played cricket until the fireflies came out into
the square and the boys went home with their bats and wickets and
balls, then he got up and caught some fireflies and put them in a
small white phial to put under his pillow so that he could watch them
glow when his parents blew out the kerosene lamp.

'Aye – no name – that is your name?'

'I name Bolan,' he said sullenly as he eyed the six or seven boys
who had stopped their game and stood about from their batting or
bowling or fielding positions waiting on him.

'Well . . . you want to play or you don't want to play? Cat bite you
tongue or what?'

His parents had left their ajoupa hut in Tunapuna and loaned out
the two cows to his uncle so that his father could work as a
cutlassman at the air bases the Americans were building at
Chaguaramas, and the boy went to the 'Market School' in the back of
the Eastern Market with its thousands of voices of buyers, vendors
and live animals screaming through the windows of the school so that
he could not hear what the teacher was saying sometimes. That cost
six lashes in the palm for what the teacher called 'day-dreaming'. And
when he finally understood what was meant by 'day-dreaming' he
could not help but feel that the teacher had pierced deep into him
and discovered a secret he kept from everyone else. Because his mind

60 *did*, indeed, run away to the smells and sounds of Tunapuna that the
crowing of a fowl in the Eastern Market stimulated. And he came to
the square in the evenings because it had in some way seemed like
the only place in the city of Port of Spain where people were not
chasing him down. It was quiet in Woodford Square, a strange
65 brooding quiet, not of loneliness or nothingness, but of someone
having been there long, long ago who had left an insignificant
footstep on the landscape. For that was Woodford Square, and the
Trinity Church beyond, and the Red House and the Public Library,
footsteps left behind by unknown people called British and Spaniards
70 who had gone back to their homes to bury their bones a long, long
time ago, leaving Woodford Square behind for him, a Tunapuna boy
from the sugarcane fields, to come to spend the evenings in.

He still sat on the runner, his long-boned hands hung down
between his knees, admitting to himself that the cricket set the boys
75 had was good, three wickets made from sawn-off broomsticks, which
they had nailed into the ground, two bats, one made from a coconut
branch, the other a real store bat that smelled of linseed oil, and a
cork ball that still had red paint on its surface. He rose, took up the
ball, and began hefting it, tossing it up in the air, then catching it to
80 feel its weight, while the other boys looked on in silence.

In Tunapuna he had played with used tennis balls which rich
people sold for six cents apiece after they had lost their bounce and
elasticity. Only on Sunday matches had he seen a real cork ball and
the touch of this one, its rough texture between his fingers, its very
85 colour, gave him a feeling of power. He knew that he could bowl
them all down for a duck with this ball.

The boys first looked at each other questioningly, then they began
moving to their playing positions as they watched the thin boy count
off fifteen paces. He turned and his feet slapped at the turf moving
90 him along like a feather; his long thin body arched like a bow, the
ball swung high in the air, his wrist turned in, and he delivered the
shooting red ball that turned pink as it raced to the batsman. The
batsman swiped blindly and missed, his head swung back quickly to
see how the ball could have gone past him so fast. 'Aye, aye, aye,' the
95 wicket-keeper cried out, as the ball smacked into his hands making

them red hot. The fielders who were scattered far off moved in closer
to see if they could catch the secret in his bowling, but each time he
sent the ball shooting through the air, they missed some small flick of
his wrist that made him bowl them all down before they could see the
100   ball.

'You want to come back and play tomorrow?' they asked as they
stood about the corner of Frederick and Prince Street, eating black
pudding and souse from a vendor who had a charcoal brazier going
on the street corner.

105   The boy jerked his shoulders up and down in an indefinite gesture
as he watched the other boys buy an inch, two inches, three inches of
the black blood sausages, sizzling in a large tray on the pale red
embers.

'How much *you* want?' the vendor asked, as he stood staring at the
110   heap of hot pink ash in the mouth of the brazier, his thumb hooked
in his pants' waist. And again he jerked his shoulders up and down in
the same indefinite gesture, and when he thought that the vendor was
about to offer him a piece of black pudding for nothing, he moved to
the back of the clique of boys and disappeared before the fat old
115   woman turned around to look for him again.

It was turning that salmon and orange light of the evening when
the sun's rays and the shadows of the trees in Woodford Square were
playing tug o' war, both stretched out thin in the evening as they
pulled upon each other until that singular moment when no one was
120   looking, and night fell upon the ground like a ball of silk cotton
descending through the air with its infinite fall until it touched the
grass and settled there as if to remain for ever. He turned into their
long tunnelled gateway on Frederick Street and walked to the far end
of the deep backyard, for theirs was the last barrack-room close to a
125   high wall that separated the yard from the next street.

As he entered the room he smelt cooking, the smoke of the
kerosene lamps, fresh cut grass from his father's clothes, and the faint
odour of cigarettes and rum that his father's body exuded.

'Boy, where you does go whole evening instead of stop home
130   here and help your moomah?' his father asked. The boy saw him only
late in the evenings now, and each evening he brought home a nip of

Black Cat rum. At first the boy thought that they were rich as they
said they would become when they left Tunapuna, where a nip of
rum meant that it was a holiday or a celebration and there was
135 laughter all around.

'Nowhere,' he answered, as he hid his phial of fireflies under the
straw mat on which he slept.

'No-way, no-way . . . You beginning to play big shot! You could
talk better than you moomah and poopah. Boy! You don't know how
140 lucky you is to be goin' to school. When I was your age . . . ' His
father left the sentence incomplete as he put the nip to his mouth and
gargled the rum as though he were rinsing out his mouth, then
swallowed it.

'Leave the child alone! If that is the way they teach him to talk in
145 school, that is the right way,' his mother put in his defence.

'Yes . . . but No-way is a place? Show me where No-way is, show
me! . . . you or he, where No-way is, where this boy does go and idle
away he time. You know where he does go?' his father shouted, and
then it was one of those moments when he felt as if he had held his
150 mother in front of him as a sort of shield to save himself from a rain
of blows.

His father then fell into one of those silences. He looked like an
old man. He let his hair grow on his head and face unless they were
going to Tunapuna. Then he would get a shave and a trim, and tell
155 everyone that he was making three dollars a day at the American
Base.

His mother meantime moved about in the series of quick motions
that came as she was close to finishing up her cooking for the
evening. She seemed to get a sudden burst of energy towards the
160 climax that would make the whole evening's preparation of dinner
come to an end with a soft breath of finality.

'The man for the room rent come and he say that next week the
price goin' up by two shillings,' she said, as if she were speaking to
herself. They lived in one of a long line of barracks that you entered
165 after passing through one of those deep dark gateways on Frederick
Street. Inside the yard was a stone 'bleach' made up of large boulders
whitened by the drying of soap as clothes were spread out in the sun

to bleach on the hot stones. There was a yellow brass pipe in the centre of the yard tied to a wooden spike driven in the ground.

170 'It look as if everything goin' up since *we* come to live in town. Is always the same damn thing. Soon as you have a shilling save . . . two shillings expense come up. As soon as we did have a li'l money save we have to go and get a . . .'

'A child?' his mother asked.

175 The boy's eyelids jerked up and his eyes met his mother's and he saw her look back quickly into the brazier.

The same feeling flooded across his heart as it had in those days he sat on the runner in the Square, waiting for something he could not describe. As he left the Square that evening he had felt suddenly
180 released from it, now it was upon him again, clinging to his eyebrows and eyelashes like those invisible cobwebs that hang from the trees in the Square in the early darkness of the evening.

'Boy, why you don't go and sleep instead of listening to big-people talk,' his father said, and the boy started to get up from the
185 low stool on which he sat.

'He ain't eat yet,' the boy's mother said. 'At least let him eat. What you want the boy to do? Go out in the road so he can't hear what you saying? It only have one room and the child have ears just like anybody else. Now come and eat too before you drink any more.'

190 The boy felt more and more that there were things which he had not noticed about his father before. The way he let a long silence linger between the moment he was spoken to, and his reply. And during a lapse like this, he would press his jaw together and make a terrible grimace, then swallow hard before he spoke again.

195 'Before I drink anymo'! Huh! It ain't *have* no mo' to drink,' his father said as he turned the small green bottle upside down, from which two or three drops of amber liquid fell on his protruding tongue.

They had finished eating their dinner in silence when his father
200 said, 'Boy, go and full this cup with water.' The boy unwound his thin long legs from his squatting position and hurried out to the pipe in the yard. He returned and handed it to his father.

'All right, boy . . . go ahead and sleep now.'

As he started over to the mat in the corner of the room where he
205 slept, his mother said, '*Boy* this . . . *boy* that! What come over you at
all? The child have a name, and it look as if you even forget that too.'

His father let his body slowly fall backwards and when he was flat
on the floor, he stretched his limbs with a sigh of relief and tiredness.
His eyeballs were dancing in a frenzy under his closed eyelids. Then
210 he spoke after a short silence.

'I too tired to argue with you . . . you hear, woman. I goin' to
sleep, so I could go and do the white people work tomorrow, please
God.'

She turned the lamp down low and went out into the yard to wash
215 the iron pots and enamel plates, and when she returned the boy
could hear her talking out loud to herself as she often did these days,
yet talking unmistakably to his father, as though she were trying to
cloud over what she was saying in a kind of slant by not speaking to
him directly.

220 'Is true,' she mumbled, 'that we ain't save much, that you believe
you work hard for nothing, but don't forget how much we had to
borrow to move to Port of Spain. One day when we pay back
everybody we will be able to save something . . .'

From the darkness he heard his father, whom he thought was
225 sound asleep, ask her, 'And how much we have save in the can?'

She took out the Capstan tin in which she kept the money, and
counted out all the coins which they had saved above all their
expenses since they had come to the city.

'It have eight shillings save up in the can,' she said, in a tone of
230 voice which the boy felt was a disappointed one, as if she too felt that
there should be more in the cigarette tin. His father let out only a
small noise, and as though he had dreamt the little incident, he went
back to sleep again.

The following evening the boy went to Woodford Square again.
235 He was a little late, for he had gone down to the foot of Frederick
Street on an errand, and when he entered the square, he saw the
boys sitting on the grass, the wickets nailed in the ground in
readiness, the bats leaning against a berry tree, and the ball at their
sides. Someone caught sight of him and shouted to the others, 'Look

240 Bolan!' and the boys all stood up now. He began running towards them, filled with an excitement such as he had never felt before.

'We was waitin' for you, man . . . what make you come so late today?' The boy was pleased beyond words that they had not started the game without him. He squeezed out a shiny red cork ball, brand
245 new, from his pocket with a wide smile on his face such as they had never seen before. They all ran to their places and they played cricket until it was dark in the square. The boy was to be their star bowler from now. At the vendor's stall afterwards, he paid for all the black puddin' they could eat.

250 'Gimmie a two-inch piece,' someone would call out, and the boy foraged in his pocket, fingering the surface of the red ball each time he reached for a coin to pay the vendor. Along the emptiness of Frederick Street they heard someone calling. The boys looked in turns to see if it might be any of their parents, then fell back to their black
255 pudding.

Suddenly the boy recognised his father in the cut-away trousers that came three-quarters of the way down his legs. 'I have to go,' he said hastily, and he ran up Frederick Street. As they turned into the gateway, his father took hold of his ear and tugged him close. 'I goin'
260 to give you a cut-ass that you go remember so long as you live,' he said, as he led the boy to the back of the yard where an old carpenter had left hundreds of switches of sawn-off wood. The boy danced up and down as the lashes rained now on his feet, now on his back. His father shouted at him, 'It ain't have no thief in my family . . . we never
265 rob nobody a black cent.' The boy's mother hovered about, trying to catch the switch from his hand, and each time she caught it, he took another from the large pile that lay about on the ground.

'All right,' his mother said. 'Nobody ain't say that your family rob anybody . . . why you don't leave the boy alone?' For each moment of
270 defence from his mother, the boy got more stinging lashes on his legs.

'And where this boy learn to thief from . . . where? Where he learnin' these *bad bad* habits from . . . not from me!' his father said.

'Don't call the child a thief . . . he is not a thief, he just take the money to buy something.'

275 'He is a thief . . . thief,' his father insisted, and the switch whistled

with each word.

'When I get through with him he never thief in he whole life again, he go remember what it mean to be a thief.' The boy's legs were marked with thin red welts from the lashes and he stopped
280 jumping up and down from the switches now. His father, too, seemed tired, and now his mother took hold of the switch in his hand.

'You ain't have no feelin's . . . you done gone and kill the half of this boy that is you half, now leave the half that make out of
285 my body, if you still have any feelin's for that.'

She took the boy to the standpipe and mixed some salt in a cup of water and made him drink it down, then she took out the ball from his pocket and the few pennies of change he had left. She had gone to the square several days looking for the boy and
290 seen him on the runner watching the other boys play, and she had gone away. When she saw the ball, she knew that they had finally asked him to play.

'You still remember how to bowl?' she asked him, and the boy nodded, his eyes fastened to the ground. After they blew out the
295 kerosene lamp the boy rolled from one side of the mat to the other, trying to find a position in which his body would not be painful. He heard his mother talking to his father in whispers, and he was afraid another beating would follow. He stopped his ears so that he would not hear their conversation, and long
300 afterwards, when he had fallen asleep with his arms around his head, he dreamt that the great green man standing in the cauldron of water in Woodford Square had moved his lips and spoken to him saying, 'I didn't know, boy . . . is for you we doin' all this . . . only you. We love you like nothin' else in the whole
305 whole world . . . must always remember that.'

And when they were all awake in the morning and he wondered if he had dreamt the words that still sang in his ears, he remembered that he had smelt his father's body as he came and lay close to him in the night.

Ruth Prawer Jhabvala

The Young Couple

Ruth Prawer Jhabvala was born in 1927 in Germany. She moved to India after her marriage to an Indian architect. Since 1955 she has written twelve novels and in 1975 she won the Booker Prize for *Heat and Dust*, subsequently winning a BAFTA for Best Screenplay for the filmed adaptation. Jhabvala received Academy Awards for her adaptations of E. M. Forster's novels, *Howards End* and *A Room with a View*.

Cathy was thrilled at going back to India with Naraian, her new husband. They had many ideas about the things Naraian would do for his country once he got back there, and all their English friends envied them because of the challenge, the life of
5   purpose, that awaited them.

On arrival, Naraian wasted no time in looking round for a job in which his skills would be properly harnessed in the service of his country. Early every morning he went out to make his contacts, leaving Cathy behind in the new flat they had rented. They had a
10   glorious view from their flat: on one side of all of the neighbouring houses, they could look right down into courtyard after courtyard and see what everyone was doing; and on the other side of a decadent, eighteenth-century mausoleum, very large, very ornate, with a vast dome which looked especially magnificent against the sunset. The flat
15   had been got for them through an uncle's influence, and they were very happy with it, even though it was small and up on the roof and very hot because of the sun beating down on it all day.

In the mornings, after Naraian had gone, Cathy wandered by herself through their two rooms and out on to the roof in her flimsy
20   nylon nightie, yawning and plaiting and unplaiting her long blonde hair. Sometimes she looked down into the courtyards, to see men shaving, servants lighting fires, sometimes at the birds wheeling round and round the dome of the mausoleum. So early in the mornings everything was still pastel coloured – the sky a pale washed blue, the

25 trees a misty green – all the things that later would become violent
    and hot. Cathy ate a bit, read a bit, let the hours slip happily by till
    she saw Naraian again. Some time during the morning the sweeper-
    woman came to clean – thin, cheerful, tattered but gaudy, with big
    silver anklets and very white pointed teeth; there was no other
30 language but smiles and nods by which she and Cathy could
    communicate so they made what they could of those. Actually, the
    sweeper-woman swept very badly indeed, but since they seemed to
    have established such friendly relations, Cathy felt shy to point this
    out to her, though Naraian sometimes did (rather too rudely and
35 loudly, Cathy thought, but the sweeper-woman never seemed to
    mind, on the contrary, she showed her pointed teeth wider, whiter
    than ever).

    In the evenings Cathy usually met Naraian in town somewhere.
    They visited a lot of restaurants, patronizing one for its South Indian
40 food, another for its ovenbaked chickens, a third for the band and the
    dance-floor. Everywhere they met friends – Naraian's friends, with
    whom he had gone to school and college and had sat about with in
    restaurants before he had left for England. All of them were restless
    and discontented, like Naraian himself, and they swore at the
45 Government, at the social set-up, at their families, at the poverty and
    backwardness of the country. Some of them had jobs, found for them
    usually through the influence of some relative, others were like
    Naraian still looking for jobs and meanwhile living at the expense of
    their families who, it appeared, kept them very well for they were all
50 expensively dressed and seemed to have plenty of pocket-money to
    spend in restaurants, cinemas, and record-shops.

    Although in England Cathy had enjoyed parties and company, here
    she always preferred to be alone with Naraian. She didn't care for
    these friends of his, she thought they were silly and spoiled; and
55 besides, or rather most of all, what galled her was their attitude to
    herself. It was true, they were polite to her, but the trouble was they
    were *too* polite, in a very formal and courtly way, so that she felt all
    the time that her presence was a strain on them and they would have
    been happier without her. Moreover, they treated her – as the wife of
60 a friend – with such undue respect, always looking shyly away from

her, never raising their eyes to her face, that she, who was young, blonde and pretty, felt slighted; especially as she knew how fervidly interested they were in women and saw how they nudged each other and their eyes became moist and dreamy whenever any passable
65   young woman hove into sight.

Naraian, on the other hand, loved being with his friends and quite often seemed to forget that Cathy was there with him. She was rather a demonstrative girl and liked kissing and holding hands with Naraian when other people were looking, and indeed in England he had
70   enjoyed that too, and they had sat in coffee bars and on park benches with their arms slung closely round each other. But here, when they were in public places, Naraian took care to see that there was a decent few inches of space always between them, and that their hands never for a moment, not even by accident, as much as touched.
75   Nor did he talk to her much when they were out together or let his eyes stray in her direction: yet he was always, she noticed, very much aware of what she was up to, for if for instance her dress had crept up over her knee or a button had come undone, he was quick to notice and by indirect means – such as clearing of throat or significant
80   glances somewhere in her direction if never directly at her – managed to draw her attention to such accidental immodesties.

Alone at home, however, he was as affectionate with her as he had always been and (perhaps it was something in the climate?) even more passionate. They spent a lot of time lying on their beds or
85   walking round the hot rooms stark naked together. This was very pleasant indeed. They could both afford to be seen uncovered, for she was a tender unflawed white, delightfully plump where necessary, full of curves and grace; and he pale brown, spare, hard, and muscular, not tall but beautifully put together. They were both very
90   young, with all their strength still intact in them. No wonder then that, when there were only the two of them together, they were always completely happy.

Unfortunately – or so it seemed to Cathy – there were not only his friends but his family too. It was not that his family were not happy
95   with Cathy: they were, they enjoyed having an English daughter-in-law, they were proud of her. When Naraian had first brought her, they

had made a splendid wedding for them, with hundreds of guests, revolving neon lights, fireworks, two bands, and several days of over-eating. Nor had they raised any objections to the young couple living

100 separately, although the family house was quite large enough to absorb a number of married sons with their young families: on the contrary, they had even helped them find this flat and pay a year's advance rent on it. The father liked to wink in a tolerant, expansive way at business friends while remarking that young people – well,

105 one had to understand, they liked to be alone, none of the old fogies around them; and the mother, too, explained that this was the way it was in modern times, young to young and old to old, that was the trend nowadays, large joint families were really quite out of fashion. Still, of course, they expected to see quite a bit of the young couple,

110 and the original idea had been that they should come to the two main meals at the family house. As the mother said, where was the sense in running two kitchens, and besides, what did poor Cathy know about our Indian preparations of which his mother knew Naraian to be so fond? But two large heavy Indian meals a day proved too much for

115 Cathy – and, after his years in England, for Naraian too – and very soon they missed out on one of them and after a while on both of them, so that in the end they found themselves going only on Sundays and on special festive occasions.

Cathy did not enjoy these obligatory Sunday lunches. First of all

120 they always had to parry some resentment, especially from the mother, who made a mouth for the first half-hour and thereafter when she remembered, and remarked that she was glad the food at home was still good enough for them at least once in the week. There were also comments from her on Naraian's appearance which, she liked to

125 hint, indicated severe under-feeding, and these merged, like the chimes of a clock, into whatever else was said during the afternoon. But it wasn't only what was said or hinted which disturbed Cathy and made her wish they could spend their Sundays in some other way: there was also a certain heaviness about the house that weighed on

130 her and made her feel oppressed, sleepy, liverish. This heaviness was physical – it was in the too rich, too abundant food, in the solid ornate pieces of furniture, in the silver, the waist-high vases, the

brocade curtains, the carpets, the giant plumped-out cushions; and in
the people themselves, the mother, large, handsome, with a proud
135 bosom draped in shimmering silk and adorned with a great deal of
golden jewellery, the father, also large, comfortable, good humoured,
very fond of his food and proud of his house and all his possessions,
among whom he liked to number Naraian and blonde English Cathy.

She could not complain that they did not care for her. The trouble
140 was they cared too much, so that she felt herself lapped around and
drowning in more love than she had ever before, among her cool
English family and friends, encountered. Everything that she and
Naraian said or did, the way they looked, everything was the subject
of scrupulous family concern, to be pointed out, discussed, wondered
145 at and advised over. Not only by the parents themselves but by all
other members of the family – of whom there were so many that
sometimes Cathy was no longer sure who they were or whether she
had met them before at all. Quite a few of them lived in the house,
and the rest dropped in throughout the day, staying for meals or
150 eating quantities of sweets and nuts in between meals, while their
cars were lined up in the drive outside with their chauffeurs squatting
under the big banyan tree and enjoying a surreptitious game of cards.

What the family discussed most vigorously was Naraian's refusal to
enter any of the family business concerns or to accept any of the jobs
155 which they kept arranging for him. They took this up with him over
and over again, every Sunday, and often – in fact, usually – the
discussions turned into a quarrel, with voices raised, tables thumped,
and once or twice it had ended with Naraian, and Cathy in tow,
storming angrily out of the house. All the way home, and indeed for
160 days afterwards, he fumed indignantly against his own family in
particular and against Indian families in general, who would not allow
a man to take his own decisions but regarded it as their right to take
them for him. Cathy heartily supported his indignation and hoped that
now he would do something decisive and independent to face the
165 family with next Sunday; but all that happened was that he discussed
the whole thing with his friends who, of course, had plenty of similar
complaints of their own, and so they all chimed together on one of
their favourite subjects – the tyranny of family domination – and next

Sunday the whole thing was repeated with identical words of anger
and perhaps with Naraian storming out of the house again.

Of course, it was not easy to do anything decisive and
independent while they were living the way they were, with Naraian's
family supporting them completely; and the most important step now
was for Naraian to get himself a job to support the two of them. But,
as they both fully agreed, it was no use rushing anything; he had to
have time to look around and weigh possibilities, so that in the end
he would have something beautiful and useful where he would be
fully engaged. In the meantime, Cathy would have been glad to help
out and get a job herself. She had done quite a lot of things in
England, she had been a receptionist to a Harley Street specialist, a
sales assistant in an airlines office, once for a brief while a waitress in
a coffee bar, but of course she realized that it was impossible to do
anything like that here because of her, or rather the family's,
background and social standing. The sort of jobs this background and
social standing permitted her she was not qualified to do.
Nevertheless, often nowadays, after Naraian had gone out, she lay on
the bed, on her stomach, one foot with a silver slipper dangling from
it up in the air, her fingers twisting and untwisting the end of her
golden plait, and read the Situations Vacant columns in the
newspapers. It was depressing: there was nothing, nothing at all for
her. It was all either for readers and senior lecturers in sociology, or
for fitters and mill-inspectors preferably with experience in small-grind
machines. Soon her eyes involuntarily slipped to the matrimonial
columns, which amused her. But she felt frustrated.

Also, perhaps, a little bored and lonely. She met plenty of people
but they were all Naraian's friends or his family, so that she began to
feel almost as if they were forming a ring round her out of which she
could not break. She confided this impression to Naraian, who
scorned it. She was free, he insisted, to do exactly as she liked, go
wherever she wanted. But where was she to go, what was there to
do? She never liked to go anywhere without Naraian, and there was
certainly no question of walking freely down the road: she was stared
at, sometimes mocked for being white and different, certainly always
an object of attention. Sometimes, when it seemed to her that she was

205 getting a complex about this, she decided to brave the stares and
taunts and go by herself into the city bazaar. Actually, it wasn't so
bad: she drew a lot of attention but she ignored it. She pretended to
merge with the crowd of modestly veiled women, sick cows,
pickpockets, and obtrusive hawkers. When she got home, she was
210 breathless but quite excited. She spread her purchases on the bed
with a feeling of triumph: they were invariably things she didn't need
– a red velvet purse sewn over with silver spangles, green and gold
sandals, a picture of a swan reflected in a lake which was made out
of a piece of mirror – but she was proud and pleased with herself for
215 having gone out to buy them.

One Sunday, at lunch with Naraian's family, she was questioned
about these excursions of hers. It seemed she had been seen (one
was always seen, there were so many relatives, so many
acquaintances, so much time in which to pass the word around) and
220 what had excited particular comment was that she had been alone
and on foot. 'Where is the need?' said Naraian's mother. 'One word,
and I shall come myself with the car to take you.' This was true:
Naraian's mother, sisters, sisters-in-law, always eager to go out
shopping in a car, frequently urged her to join them. But she had
225 enjoyed herself more on her own. She looked for help to Naraian, but
he was busy eating a mango; either he hadn't heard, or he didn't want
to get involved. She would have welcomed a word from him to tell
his family about the independence customarily enjoyed as a right by
English girls.

230 No such word coming, Naraian's mother drove her point home
further: 'Our girls don't go into these bazaars alone. It is not proper
for us.'

There was a waiting pause. Cathy knew she was now expected to
make a tart reply which would instigate her mother-in-law to an even
235 tarter one, after which it would be her turn again, and so on until
they had got a really good family row going. But Cathy didn't say
anything. Unlike the others, she had no liking for these family rows.
Instead she looked again towards Naraian who was now busy eating
the flesh round the stone of his mango, always a delicate operation
240 calling for all one's concentration and skill. Cathy lowered her head,

lifted the napkin from her lap, and folded it several times very neatly. She sensed disappointment in the air, as if she had let everyone down.

But it was she who felt let down. That night, after an hour or two
245 of sleeplessness, she woke Naraian up quite roughly: 'You could have said something,' she said. 'Instead of sitting there with that damn mango.'

She knew at once, though it was dark and she couldn't see his face, that he had caught on. Perhaps he had been harbouring a bad
250 conscience. But all he said was, 'What's the matter with you? In the middle of the night.' He yawned and tried to go back to sleep. But she turned on the light.

'Throwing me to the wolves,' she grumbled.

He blinked against the light, but sat up. His chest and shoulders
255 were naked, smooth, and brown.

'You could have *said* something.'

'What? What could I have said?' He put one arm round her; she was wearing a low-cut pink nylon nightie with a lace top, and her blonde hair hung loose about her shoulders. She leaned against him:
260 'I felt so awful. As if they were all going to attack me or something.'

'Silly girl.' He drew her closer against himself, kissed her hair. She felt comforted and soothed.

'The way she was carrying on,' she said, with a pout now that she felt she had an ally, even though a belated one. 'Really, I mean, what
265 had I *done*? I hope it's not a crime to go out, is it?' And when he didn't say anything, she gave him a jab and looked sharply up at him: 'Well, *is* it?'

He uttered an uneasy laugh: 'Crime, crime – how you talk, Cathy.'

She freed herself from his arm and shouted: 'I could have hit you!
270 The way you sat there sucking that mango!'

Then he became prim, his lips were narrow and his nostrils pinched: 'Perhaps she was not as wrong as you think'; and when she said nothing, only stared at him in shocked unbelief, he became even more righteous: 'It's not Oxford Street, you know. You can't just
275 saunter down the road as you please.' He looked at her out of the corner of his eye, then decided to be bold: turned out the light, and

lay on his other side to go back to sleep. He was waiting but there was no sign from her, so soon he really was asleep again.

280 She continued to spend her days as she had done before – padding round the flat on naked feet, stretching, yawning, plaiting and unplaiting her hair; but whereas before she had felt time lapping deliciously round her in endless honeyed hours, now her feelings were ones of boredom. The endless hours were harsh not honeyed now. When she sank down on her bed, it was not in enjoyment, soft,

285 languid, stretching herself, but in a dry boredom with nothing to do, nothing to think, and many hours yet till it was time to meet Naraian. And even when she did meet him – she was bored with the restaurants now, she knew all the bearers down to the stains on each one's uniform, had eaten all the dishes on the menu and found them

290 all tasting the same, the band was no longer a gay, slick group called the Merry Macs but a collection of tired men who lived in a room above the restaurant and worried about their next engagement. And Naraian and his friends still sat there, eating, drinking, smoking, condemning everything as it was now but looking forward to a future

295 when each one had his desires and the world would be moulded by such as they.

Cathy and Naraian began to bicker. Naraian complained about the way she kept the flat – he said everything was dirty and untidy, he stumbled over pieces of discarded underwear, and where once he

300 would have tenderly picked them up and even perhaps pressed them to his lips, now he kicked them aside impatiently, at the same time shouting at her to point out her neglect. He also shouted at the sweeper-woman more often than ever, and when Cathy interfered, he turned on her instead and soon they would be shouting at each other,

305 while it was the sweeper-woman who tried to calm them by pursing her lips and cooing sweet words into the air, as if she were soothing two ruffled pet birds in a cage.

Not for pleasure so much as in defiance, Cathy went out more frequently by herself. She visited the city bazaar several times,

310 although there was nothing she wanted to buy and it was hot, crowded, full of smells most of which were unpleasant, and sly men with dirty fingers touched her surreptitiously from out of the crowd.

Once or twice she sat on a public bus and went far out to some place of historical interest, some ruined tower or palace or mosque, and here she was happy for a while amid green grass, old stone, and silence: although what she always looked forward to most was going back home and telling Naraian where she had been. At first he used to protest, would even try and forbid her from taking these solitary excursions, but she was ready for him, opposed him with such spirit, such defiance, such *enjoyment*, that he had to retreat. But then a reaction would set in for her, and she would be sad at her victory – or rather, at his defeat. She did not like to see him overcome, even by herself, and when he turned away and said do what you like in a resigned voice, she flung herself round his neck and kissed his face all over, crying at the same time, 'If you don't want me to, I won't, I won't', and they clung together, whispered together, and soon they were lying on their bed together, fervently forgiving each other.

Always somewhat confused about dates, it took Cathy longer than it should have done to find out she was pregnant. From then on a big fuss was made of her. The family priest performed various ceremonies, and her mother-in-law and sisters-in-law took her to the best doctor. Many special dishes were cooked for her, she was exhorted to take great quantities of milk, food, and rest, and generally to pamper herself in every possible way. This she did. She spent most of her time sitting at the window of their flat looking out. Sometimes she looked out at the left side, into all the neighbouring courtyards; but what she liked best was to look out at the right side, at the mausoleum, to see the birds wheeling round its dome, and the tops of trees with the leaves looking very green, young, and tender against the weathered stone, and the sky a brilliant blue the whole day long until it faded away at dusk. She sat there hour after hour, her cheek supported on her hand. She looked forward to having a baby, to the future, to Naraian having a job and doing wonderful things. She was glad to be young and married to Naraian. 'Her cup of happiness was full,' she kept repeating to herself, it chimed in her head like a tune, she turned it over and over and smiled at it. She slept a lot, a delicious drowsiness stealing over her like kisses from a god; she stopped going out, even in the evenings when she was usually too

tired to go and meet Naraian. Instead he would come home earlier,
350 leaving his friends behind in the restaurant, and he would always
bring something for her to eat for which she had expressed a liking,
although there was plenty of food for her sent over from his father's
house. If she was asleep, he woke her up and supported her in bed
and fed her, bite by bite, and kissed the top of her head in satisfaction
355 while she ate. If he found clothes strewn about the place, he picked
them up and folded them, moving very softly so as not to disturb her.

All the week she felt fine, never better, but on Sunday mornings
she always woke up sick. In between vomits, she kept saying, 'I can't
go.' He said soothingly, 'You'll feel better in a minute.' Both of them
360 knew she wouldn't, but both of them also knew that they would have
to go. Naraian's father always sent a car for them. The car-ride made
her feel worse than ever, but when she arrived at the house, the
mother and the other ladies in the house and the female servants
smiled triumphantly to see her in this state. Yes, they said, that was
365 the way it was in pregnancy (and they all of them knew all about
pregnancy), no use complaining, one just had to put up with it. And
anyway, they added, nodding approvingly at her queasiness, it was a
healthy sign, and they pinched her cheek and patted her and found
her altogether to their satisfaction. But she couldn't bear them near
370 her with their smell of hair-oil, perspiration, and rich food – a smell
indeed that pervaded the whole house till she felt it would drive her
mad and she had to rush out into the garden. But here too she felt
oppressed in the same way as she did in the house, for the smells
from the creepers and the flowers were too rich, and the flowers
375 themselves, fed with too much fertilizer, too thick and fleshy.

One Sunday there was a surprise for her. It was a more than
usually crowded Sunday, with a lot of uncles present, and there was
evidently much to discuss. Naraian too was part of the discussion, in
fact, he seemed to be the centre of it, and she glanced over at him
380 wondering what was going on, and once or twice he glanced back at
her with a hint, she thought, of uneasiness. But everyone else seemed
to be pleased, the father smoked a fat cigar and smiled complacently
round it, and the mother too was smiling, she was very tender with
Cathy, patted and fondled her hands, saying, 'Now everything will be

385   nice for you.' And an aunt said, 'Such a fine salary too, it is a great
      chance for him,' whereupon the mother retorted, with a trace of
      sharpness in her voice, 'Naturally, a clever boy like that, five years in
      England, it is his due.' Cathy caught Naraian's eye again; he looked
      away quickly. She was very miserable; she shut her eyes but she
390   couldn't shut out the sense of this large, well-fed family with Naraian
      and herself trapped in the middle of them.

      But she should have been glad, not miserable. What was she
      complaining about? he asked her, as soon as they were home again.
      At last he had a job, and moreover a well-paid one, and now they
395   could be as independent as she had always wanted them to be. She
      shook her head: she couldn't or wouldn't put her feelings about this
      job into words. 'It has a lot of scope,' he urged and looked at her
      anxiously, and when she refused to respond, he took on a defiant
      little swagger: 'You don't get a salary like that every day.' Cathy began
400   to cry; very quietly tears rolled down her cheeks. Seeing these, he lost
      his temper, he shouted 'You're mad!' but there was pain in his voice,
      for he too was disappointed that finally, after all the tall talk, he
      should have ended up with a job in his uncle's firm. She tried to stop
      crying but she couldn't, the tears came faster and faster, nor did she
405   have a handkerchief to wipe them with, so that she had to do so on
      her bare arm, burying her face in it and making dirty tear-streaks all
      down her cheeks. Her nose too had begun to run. In anger and
      disgust, he drew a handkerchief out of his pocket and threw it at her
      and she took it gratefully; she tried to explain to him, tried to disguise
410   the cause of her tears now that she saw so clearly that he too was
      hurt, but she was too far gone to be able to speak coherently, and
      instead of words deep sobs rose out of her chest. He turned away
      from her, left the room, the flat, banging the door behind him, and in
      despair she heard his footsteps running away from her down the
415   stone staircase.

      As it happened, however, he enjoyed his job. He sat in an air-
      conditioned office all day, had a peon to himself and a share in a
      secretary, attended board meetings, and entertained at business
      lunches. He came home in the evenings, tired but satisfied, and took
420   pleasure in telling her his day's doings. They rarely went out in the

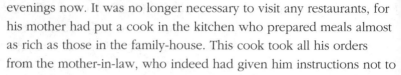

evenings now. It was no longer necessary to visit any restaurants, for his mother had put a cook in the kitchen who prepared meals almost as rich as those in the family-house. This cook took all his orders from the mother-in-law, who indeed had given him instructions not to
425 bother Cathy because of her delicate state. This suited Cathy very well; in any case, she hardly partook of any of his preparations but fed herself on cream crackers and bars of chocolate. The cook quarrelled a lot with the sweeper-woman, and the mother-in-law, who came at least once every day, participated in these quarrels.
430 Altogether she took a great interest in everything that happened in the flat and poked around in the cupboards and even under the bed to see what went on there. She found a lot of things amiss, in fact, almost everything. The flat and its shortcomings now became the chief topic of discussion at the Sunday meals.
435   Cathy shut her ears to it, as much as she could. She would not be drawn. She heard how the flat was uncomfortable, unsanitary, an unnecessary expense – and those stairs! For a woman in her condition! She kept quiet: she knew that, among these adepts, she would always be outwitted in argument – or rather, shouted down,
440 which counted as the same thing. But it irked her that Naraian did not come to the defence of their nest as vigorously as she felt he might have done. He parried the thrusts now and again but, it was to be noticed, half-heartedly, so that the mother was always left in clear possession of the field. There were no more rousing family rows the
445 way there had been when it had been a question of Naraian's taking a job; no more banging of doors, storming out of the house with Cathy in tow, the two of them brave young champions against the combined mass and power of the rest of the family. Now, Cathy felt, no one was against anyone; it was as if they had joined forces.
450   And indeed, Cathy was beginning to notice more and more that Naraian was himself dissatisfied with their home. Apart from complaining about the way it was kept, he complained about the place itself too: it was hot, the construction was cheap, the whitewash flaked off the walls, the stairs were dark, narrow, and dangerous, the
455 water did not rise properly into the taps. All this was true but it hadn't mattered to them before, they had been so proud to have a place of

their own. He didn't seem to remember that; or perhaps it was a part
of his life that he had outgrown the way he had outgrown some other
things too. For instance, he no longer roamed naked round the flat
460 with Cathy, and, when she did it, he told her not to. He also seemed
to have outgrown all the friends with whom he had sat in restaurants.
He hardly ever went to meet them now. Sometimes she asked him
why not, and then he made a face to show that they were no longer
quite good enough for him. She was sorry. She hadn't liked them and
465 yet something young and nice had gone out of Naraian's life with
them. And something else went out of life when one day Naraian
dismissed their old sweeper-woman. Cathy was sad and wished for
her back, though she could not complain that the woman's dismissal
had put her to any inconvenience, for the very next day Naraian's
470 mother sent another sweeper whom she had trained herself to clean
in corners and to use Vim.

At the same time a large bedroom and dressing-room were being
got ready for them in the family-house. Everyone tried to keep it
secret from Cathy, but it was all done with such glee – a great deal of
475 whispering always went on, and Naraian was beckoned into the
room, and there were winks and veiled allusions – that her suspicions
were soon aroused. When at home she confronted Naraian with
these, he tried to hedge and say it was only if they wanted to stay
over weekends or take naps on Sunday afternoons. Soon, however,
480 he was speaking out more clearly and he said, did she think he was
going to put up with a place like this for ever? and he kicked a door
so that its poor, cheap wood splintered a bit further. And the only
thing Cathy could think of in defence was, but look at the view! and
pointed towards the dome of the mausoleum darkening against a
485 tender flush of sunset and a formation of birds, wings a-tilt, going
round it swift as bats in a last flight before plunging down into the
trees to settle themselves to sleep.

In reply, Naraian pulled a contemptuous face which made it clear
what sort of importance he attached to the view. But this expression –
490 though an honest, spontaneous one – he held for only a moment; the
next he had corrected it, looked in fact sympathetic. Probably he had
recollected the way they had once used to talk, the art galleries they

had visited in England, the plays they had witnessed, the opinions they had so seriously held on life and how to live it.

495 'What does it matter, Cathy,' he said, putting his arm round her, and his voice was tender, and so was the way he looked at her, 'what does it matter *where* we are as long as we are together?'

They kissed. This kiss was delicious but, even while it was going on and set within it as in a heartshaped frame, she had a vision of the
500 room that was being got ready for them: the same heavy, shiny furniture as the rest of the house, a carpet, ample satin bedspreads matching the curtains.

R. K. Narayan

INDIA

Leela's Friend

R. K. Narayan was born in Madras in 1906. His first novel *Swami and Friends*, was set in the fictional town of Malgudi, which he then used as a setting for subsequent novels. He has also published five collections of short stories, two travel books, four collections of essays, a memoir and some translations of Indian epics and myths.

Sidda was hanging about the gate at a moment when Mr Sivasanker was standing in the front veranda of his house, brooding over the servant problem.

'Sir, do you want a servant?' Sidda asked.

5   'Come in,' said Mr Sivasanker. As Sidda opened the gate and came in, Mr Sivasanker subjected him to a scrutiny and said to himself, 'Doesn't seem to be a bad sort . . . At any rate, the fellow looks tidy.'

'Where were you before?' he asked.

Sidda said, 'In a bungalow there,' and indicated a vague
10   somewhere, 'in the doctor's house.'

'What is his name?'

'I don't know, master,' Sidda said. 'He lives near the market.'

'Why did they send you away?'

'They left the town, master,' Sidda said, giving the stock reply.
15   Mr Sivasanker was unable to make up his mind. He called his wife. She looked at Sidda and said, 'He doesn't seem to me worse than the others we have had.' Leela, their five-year-old daughter, came out, looked at Sidda and gave a cry of joy. 'Oh, Father!' she said, 'I like him. Don't send him away. Let us keep him in our house.' And
20   that decided it.

Sidda was given two meals a day and four rupees a month, in return for which he washed clothes, tended the garden, ran errands, chopped wood and looked after Leela.

'Sidda, come and play!' Leela would cry, and Sidda had to drop
25   any work he might be doing and run to her, as she stood in the front

garden with a red ball in her hand. His company made her supremely happy. She flung the ball at him and he flung it back. And then she said, 'Now throw the ball into the sky.' Sidda clutched the ball, closed his eyes for a second and threw the ball up. When the ball came

30 down again, he said, 'Now this has touched the moon and come. You see here a little bit of the moon sticking.' Leela keenly examined the ball for traces of the moon and said, 'I don't see it.'

'You must be very quick about it,' said Sidda, 'because it will all evaporate and go back to the moon. Now hurry up . . .' He covered

35 the ball tightly with his fingers and allowed her to peep through a little gap.

'Ah, yes,' said Leela. 'I see the moon, but is the moon very wet?'

'Certainly, it is,' Sidda said.

'What is in the sky, Sidda?'

40 'God,' he said.

'If we stand on the roof and stretch our arm, can we touch the sky?'

'Not if we stand on the roof here,' he said. 'But if you stand on a coconut tree you can touch the sky.'

45 'Have you done it?' asked Leela.

'Yes, many times,' said Sidda. 'Whenever there is a big moon, I climb a coconut tree and touch it.'

'Does the moon know you?'

'Yes, very well. Now come with me. I will show you something

50 nice.' They were standing near the rose plant. He said, pointing, 'You see the moon there, don't you?'

'Yes.'

'Now come with me,' he said, and took her to the back yard. He stopped near the well and pointed up. The moon was there, too.

55 Leela clapped her hands and screamed in wonder, 'The moon here! It was there! How is it?'

'I have asked it to follow us about.'

Leela ran in and told her mother, 'Sidda knows the moon.' At dusk he carried her in and she held a class for him. She had a box filled with

60 catalogues, illustrated books and stumps of pencils. It gave her great

joy to play the teacher to Sidda. She made him squat on the floor with a pencil between his fingers and a catalogue in front of him. She had another pencil and a catalogue and commanded, 'Now write.' And he had to try and copy whatever she wrote in the pages of her catalogue.

65 She knew two or three letters of the alphabet and could draw a kind of cat and crow. But none of these could Sidda copy even remotely. She said, examining his effort, 'Is this how I have drawn the crow? Is this how I have drawn the *B*?' She pitied him and redoubled her efforts to teach him. But that good fellow, though an adept at

70 controlling the moon, was utterly incapable of plying the pencil. Consequently, it looked as though Leela would keep him there pinned to his seat till his stiff, inflexible wrist cracked. He sought relief by saying, 'I think your mother is calling you in to dinner.' Leela would drop the pencil and run out of the room, and the school hour

75 would end.

After dinner Leela ran to her bed. Sidda had to be ready with a story. He sat down on the floor near the bed and told incomparable stories: of animals in the jungle, of gods in heaven, of magicians who could conjure up golden castles and fill them with little princesses and

80 their pets . . .

Day by day she clung closer to him. She insisted upon having his company all her waking hours. She was at his side when he was working in the garden or chopping wood, and accompanied him when he was sent on errands.

85 One evening he went out to buy sugar and Leela went with him. When they came home, Leela's mother noticed that a gold chain Leela had been wearing was missing. 'Where is your chain?' Leela looked into her shirt, searched and said, 'I don't know.' Her mother gave her a slap and said, 'How many times have I told you to take it off and

90 put it in the box?'

'Sidda, Sidda!' she shouted a moment later. As Sidda came in, Leela's mother threw a glance at him and thought the fellow already looked queer. She asked him about the chain. His throat went dry. He blinked and answered that he did not know. She mentioned the

95 police and shouted at him. She had to go back into the kitchen for a moment because she had left something in the oven. Leela followed

her, whining, 'Give me some sugar, Mother, I am hungry.' When they came out again and called, 'Sidda, Sidda!' there was no answer. Sidda had vanished into the night.

100   Mr Sivasanker came home an hour later, grew very excited over all this, went to the police station and lodged a complaint.

After her meal Leela refused to go to bed. 'I won't sleep unless Sidda comes and tells me stories . . . I don't like you, Mother. You are always abusing and worrying Sidda. Why are you so rough?'

105   'But he has taken away your chain . . .'

'Let him. It doesn't matter. Tell me a story.'

'Sleep, sleep,' said Mother, attempting to make her lie down on her lap.

'Tell me a story, Mother,' Leela said. It was utterly impossible for
110 her mother to think of a story now. Her mind was disturbed. The thought of Sidda made her panicky. The fellow, with his knowledge of the household, might come in at night and loot. She shuddered to think what a villain she had been harboring all these days. It was God's mercy that he hadn't killed the child for the chain . . . 'Sleep,
115 Leela, sleep,' she cajoled.

'Can't you tell the story of the elephant?' Leela asked.

'No.'

Leela made a noise of deprecation and asked, 'Why should not Sidda sit in our chair, Mother?' Mother didn't answer the question.
120 Leela said a moment later, 'Sidda is gone because he wouldn't be allowed to sleep inside the house just as we do. Why should he always be made to sleep outside the house, Mother? I think he is angry with us, Mother.'

By the time Sivasanker returned, Leela had fallen asleep. He said,
125 'What a risk we took in engaging that fellow. It seems he is an old criminal. He has been in jail half a dozen times for stealing jewellery from children. From the description I gave, the inspector was able to identify him in a moment.'

'Where is he now?' asked the wife.
130 'The police know his haunts. They will pick him up very soon, don't worry. The inspector was furious that I didn't consult him before employing him . . .'

Four days later, just as Father was coming home from the office, a police inspector and a constable brought in Sidda. Sidda stood with
135 bowed head. Leela was overjoyed. 'Sidda! Sidda!' she cried, and ran down the steps to meet him.

'Don't go near him,' the inspector said, stopping her.

'Why not?'

'He is a thief. He has taken away your gold chain.'

140 'Let him. I will have a new chain,' Leela said, and all of them laughed. And then Mr Sivasanker spoke to Sidda; and then his wife addressed him with a few words on his treachery. They then asked him where he had put the chain.

'I have not taken it,' Sidda said feebly, looking at the ground.

145 'Why did you run away without telling us?' asked Leela's mother. There was no answer.

Leela's face became red. 'Oh, policemen, leave him alone. I want to play with him.'

'My dear child,' said the police inspector, 'he is a thief.'

150 'Let him be,' Leela replied haughtily.

'What a devil you must be to steal a thing from such an innocent child!' remarked the inspector. 'Even now it is not too late. Return it. I will let you off, provided you promise not to do such a thing again.' Leela's father and mother, too, joined in this appeal. Leela felt
155 disgusted with the whole business and said, 'Leave him alone, he hasn't taken the chain.'

'You are not at all a reliable prosecution witness, my child,' observed the inspector humorously.

'No, he hasn't taken it!' Leela screamed.

160 Her father said, 'Baby, if you don't behave, I will be very angry with you.'

Half an hour later the inspector said to the constable, 'Take him to the station. I think I shall have to sit with him tonight.' The constable took Sidda by the hand and turned to go. Leela ran behind them
165 crying, 'Don't take him. Leave him here, leave him here.' She clung to Sidda's hand. He looked at her mutely, like an animal. Mr Sivasanker carried Leela back into the house. Leela was in tears.

Every day when Mr Sivasanker came home he was asked by his

wife, 'Any news of the jewel?' and by his daughter, 'Where is Sidda?'

170 'They still have him in the lockup, though he is very stubborn and won't say anything about the jewel,' said Mr Sivasanker.

'Bah! What a rough fellow he must be!' said his wife with a shiver.

'Oh, these fellows who have been in jail once or twice lose all fear. Nothing can make them confess.'

175 A few days later, putting her hand into the tamarind pot in the kitchen, Leela's mother picked up the chain. She took it to the tap and washed off the coating of tamarind on it. It was unmistakably Leela's chain. When it was shown to her, Leela said, 'Give it here. I want to wear the chain.'

180 'How did it get into the tamarind pot?' Mother asked.

'Somehow,' replied Leela.

'Did you put it in?' asked Mother.

'Yes.'

'When?'

185 'Long ago, the other day.'

'Why didn't you say so before?'

'I don't know,' said Leela.

When Father came home and was told, he said, 'The child must not have any chain hereafter. Didn't I tell you that I saw her carrying

190 it in her hand once or twice? She must have dropped it into the pot sometime . . . And all this bother on account of her.'

'What about Sidda?' asked Mother.

'I will tell the inspector tomorrow . . . in any case, we couldn't have kept a criminal like him in the house.'

Anita Desai

INDIA

Games at Twilight

Anita Desai was born in 1937 in India to a German mother and an Indian father. She has written many novels, short stories and children's books – including *Clear Light of Day*, *In Custody* and *Fasting, Feasting* – exploring tensions within the family, amongst other themes. *The Village by the Sea* won the Guardian Award for children's fiction in 1982. Anita Desai writes in English, saying, 'I first learned English when I went to school. It was the first language that I learned to read and write, so it became my literary language.' She is currently Professor on the Creative Writing course at the Massachusetts Institute of Technology and a Fellow of Girton College, Cambridge.

It was still too hot to play outdoors. They had had their tea, they had been washed and had their hair brushed, and after the long day of confinement in the house that was not cool but at least a protection from the sun, the children strained to get out. Their faces
5   were red and bloated with the effort, but their mother would not open the door, everything was still curtained and shuttered in a way that stifled the children, made them feel that their lungs were stuffed with cotton wool and their noses with dust and if they didn't burst out into the light and see the sun and feel the air, they would choke.
10   'Please, ma, please,' they begged. 'We'll play in the veranda and porch – we won't go a step out of the porch.'

'You will, I know you will, and then – '

'No – we won't, we won't,' they wailed so horrendously that she actually let down the bolt of the front door so that they burst out like
15   seeds from a crackling, over-ripe pod into the veranda, with such wild, maniacal yells that she retreated to her bath and the shower of talcum powder and the fresh sari that were to help her face the summer evening.

They faced the afternoon. It was too hot. Too bright. The white walls

20 of the veranda glared stridently in the sun. The bougainvillea hung
about it, purple and magenta, in livid balloons. The garden outside
was like a tray made of beaten brass, flattened out on the red gravel
and the stony soil in all shades of metal – aluminium, tin, copper and
brass. No life stirred at this arid time of day – the birds still drooped,
25 like dead fruit, in the papery tents of the trees; some squirrels lay limp
on the wet earth under the garden tap. The outdoor dog lay stretched
as if dead on the veranda mat, his paws and ears and tail all reaching
out like dying travellers in search of water. He rolled his eyes at the
children – two white marbles rolling in the purple sockets, begging
30 for sympathy – and attempted to lift his tail in a wag but could not. It
only twitched and lay still.

Then, perhaps roused by the shrieks of the children, a band of
parrots suddenly fell out of the eucalyptus tree, tumbled frantically in
the still, sizzling air, then sorted themselves out into battle formation
35 and streaked away across the white sky.

The children, too, felt released. They too began tumbling, shoving,
pushing against each other, frantic to start. Start what? Start their
business. The business of the children's day which is – play.

'Let's play hide-and-seek.'
40 'Who'll be It?'
'You be It.'
'Why should I? You be – '
'You're the eldest – '
'That doesn't mean – '
45 The shoves became harder. Some kicked out. The motherly Mira
intervened. She pulled the boys roughly apart. There was a tearing
sound of cloth but it was lost in the heavy panting and angry
grumbling and no one paid attention to the small sleeve hanging
loosely off a shoulder.
50 'Make a circle, make a circle!' she shouted, firmly pulling and
pushing till a kind of vague circle was formed. 'Now clap!' she roared
and, clapping, they all chanted in melancholy unison: 'Dip, dip, dip –
my blue ship – ' and every now and then one or the other saw he
was safe by the way his hands fell at the crucial moment – palm on
55 palm, or back of hand on palm – and dropped out of the circle with a

yell and a jump of relief and jubilation.

Raghu was It. He started to protest, to cry, 'You cheated – Mira cheated – Anu cheated – ' but it was too late, the others had all already streaked away. There was no one to hear when he called out,

60 'Only in the veranda – the porch – Ma said – Ma *said* to stay in the porch!' No one had stopped to listen, all he saw were their brown legs flashing through the dusty shrubs, scrambling up brick walls, leaping over compost heaps and hedges, and then the porch stood empty in the purple shade of the bougainvillea and the garden was as

65 empty as before; even the limp squirrels had whisked away, leaving everything gleaming, brassy and bare.

Only small Manu suddenly reappeared, as if he had dropped out of an invisible cloud or from a bird's claws, and stood for a moment in the centre of the yellow lawn, chewing his finger and near to tears

70 as he heard Raghu shouting, with his head pressed against the veranda wall, 'Eighty-three, eighty-five, eighty-nine, ninety . . .' and then made off in a panic, half of him wanting to fly north, the other half counselling south. Raghu turned just in time to see the flash of his white shorts and the uncertain skittering of his red sandals, and

75 charged after him with such a blood-curdling yell that Manu stumbled over the hosepipe, fell into its rubber coils and lay there weeping, 'I won't be It – you have to find them all – all – All!'

'I know I have to, idiot,' Raghu said, superciliously kicking him with his toe. 'You're dead,' he said with satisfaction, licking the beads

80 of perspiration off his upper lip, and then stalked off in search of worthier prey, whistling spiritedly so that the hiders should hear and tremble.

Ravi heard the whistling and picked his nose in a panic, trying to find comfort by burrowing the finger deep-deep into that soft tunnel. He

85 felt himself too exposed, sitting on an upturned flower pot behind the garage. Where could he burrow? He could run around the garage if he heard Raghu come – around and around and around – but he hadn't much faith in his short legs when matched against Raghu's long, hefty, hairy footballer legs. Ravi had a frightening glimpse of

90 them as Raghu combed the hedge of crotons and hibiscus, trampling

delicate ferns underfoot as he did so. Ravi looked about him desperately, swallowing a small ball of snot in his fear.

The garage was locked with a great heavy lock to which the driver had the key in his room, hanging from a nail on the wall under his
95 work-shirt. Ravi had peeped in and seen him still sprawling on his string-cot in his vest and striped underpants, the hair on his chest and the hair in his nose shaking with the vibrations of his phlegm-obstructed snores. Ravi had wished he were tall enough, big enough to reach the key on the nail, but it was impossible, beyond his reach
100 for years to come. He had sidled away and sat dejectedly on the flower pot. That at least was cut to his own size.

But next to the garage was another shed with a big green door. Also locked. No one even knew who had the key to the lock. That shed wasn't opened more than once a year when Ma turned out all
105 the old broken bits of furniture and rolls of matting and leaking buckets, and the white ant hills were broken and swept away and Flit sprayed into the spider webs and rat holes so that the whole operation was like the looting of a poor, ruined and conquered city. The green leaves of the door sagged. They were nearly off their rusty
110 hinges. The hinges were large and made a small gap between the door and the walls – only just large enough for rats, dogs and, possibly, Ravi to slip through.

Ravi had never cared to enter such a dark and depressing mortuary of defunct household goods seething with such unspeakable
115 and alarming animal life but, as Raghu's whistling grew angrier and sharper and his crashing and storming in the hedge wilder, Ravi suddenly slipped off the flower pot and through the crack and was gone. He chuckled aloud with astonishment at his own temerity so that Raghu came out of the hedge, stood silent with his hands on his
120 hips, listening, and finally shouted 'I heard you! I'm coming! *Got* you – ' and came charging round the garage only to find the upturned flower pot, the yellow dust, the crawling of white ants in a mud-hill against the closed shed door – nothing. Snarling, he bent to pick up a stick and went off, whacking it against the garage and shed walls as if
125 to beat out his prey.

*

Ravi shook, then shivered with delight, with self-congratulation. Also with fear. It was dark, spooky in the shed. It had a muffled smell, as of graves. Ravi had once got locked into the linen cupboard and sat there weeping for half an hour before he was rescued. But at least
130 that had been a familiar place, and even smelt pleasantly of starch, laundry and, reassuringly, of his mother. But the shed smelt of rats, ant hills, dust and spider webs. Also of less definable, less recognizable horrors. And it was dark. Except for the white-hot cracks along the door, there was no light. The roof was very low. Although
135 Ravi was small, he felt as if he could reach up and touch it with his finger tips. But he didn't stretch. He hunched himself into a ball so as not to bump into anything, touch or feel anything. What might there not be to touch him and feel him as he stood there, trying to see in the dark? Something cold, or slimy – like a snake. Snakes! He leapt up
140 as Raghu whacked the wall with his stick – then, quickly realizing what it was, felt almost relieved to hear Raghu, hear his stick. It made him feel protected.

But Raghu soon moved away. There wasn't a sound once his footsteps had gone around the garage and disappeared. Ravi stood
145 frozen inside the shed. Then he shivered all over. Something had tickled the back of his neck. It took him a while to pick up the courage to lift his hand and explore. It was an insect – perhaps a spider – exploring *him*. He squashed it and wondered how many more creatures were watching him, waiting to reach out and touch
150 him, the stranger.

There was nothing now. After standing in that position – his hand still on his neck, feeling the wet splodge of the squashed spider gradually dry – for minutes, hours, his legs began to tremble with the effort, the inaction. By now he could see enough in the dark to make
155 out the large solid shapes of old wardrobes, broken buckets and bedsteads piled on top of each other around him. He recognized an old bathtub – patches of enamel glimmered at him and at last he lowered himself onto its edge.

He contemplated slipping out of the shed and into the fray. He
160 wondered if it would not be better to be captured by Raghu and be returned to the milling crowd as long as he could be in the sun, the

light, the free spaces of the garden and the familiarity of his brothers, sisters and cousins. It would be evening soon. Their games would become legitimate. The parents would sit out on the lawn on cane
165 basket chairs and watch them as they tore around the garden or gathered in knots to share a loot of mulberries or black, teeth-splitting *jamun* from the garden trees. The gardener would fix the hosepipe to the water tap and water would fall lavishly through the air to the ground, soaking the dry yellow grass and the red gravel and arousing
170 the sweet, the intoxicating scent of water on dry earth – that loveliest scent in the world. Ravi sniffed for a whiff of it. He half-rose from the bathtub, then heard the despairing scream of one of the girls as Raghu bore down upon her. There was the sound of a crash, and of rolling about in the bushes, the shrubs, then screams and accusing sobs of, 'I
175 touched the den – ' 'You did not – ' 'I did – ' 'You liar, you did *not*' and then a fading away and silence again.

Ravi sat back on the harsh edge of the tub, deciding to hold out a bit longer. What fun if they were all found and caught – he alone left unconquered! He had never known that sensation. Nothing more
180 wonderful had ever happened to him than being taken out by an uncle and bought a whole slab of chocolate all to himself, or being flung into the soda-man's pony cart and driven up to the gate by the friendly driver with the red beard and pointed ears. To defeat Raghu – that hirsute, hoarse-voiced football champion – and to be the winner
185 in a circle of older, bigger, luckier children – that would be thrilling beyond imagination. He hugged his knees together and smiled to himself almost shyly at the thought of so much victory, such laurels.

There he sat smiling, knocking his heels against the bathtub, now and then getting up and going to the door to put his ear to the broad
190 crack and listening for sounds of the game, the pursuer and the pursued, and then returning to his seat with the dogged determination of the true winner, a breaker of records, a champion.

It grew darker in the shed as the light at the door grew softer, fuzzier, turned to a kind of crumbling yellow pollen that turned to
195 yellow fur, blue fur, grey fur. Evening. Twilight. The sound of water gushing, falling. The scent of earth receiving water, slaking its thirst in

great gulps and releasing that green scent of freshness, coolness.
Through the crack Ravi saw the long purple shadows of the shed and
the garage lying still across the yard. Beyond that, the white walls of
200 the house. The bougainvillea had lost its lividity, hung in dark
bundles that quaked and twittered and seethed with masses of
homing sparrows. The lawn was shut off from his view. Could he
hear the children's voices? It seemed to him that he could. It seemed
to him that he could hear them chanting, singing, laughing. But what
205 about the game? What had happened? Could it be over? How could it
when he was still not found?

It then occurred to him that he could have slipped out long ago,
dashed across the yard to the veranda and touched the 'den'. It was
necessary to do that to win. He had forgotten. He had only
210 remembered the part of hiding and trying to elude the seeker. He had
done that so successfully, his success had occupied him so wholly
that he had quite forgotten that success had to be clinched by that
final dash to victory and the ringing cry of 'Den!'

With a whimper he burst through the crack, fell on his knees, got
215 up and stumbled on stiff, benumbed legs across the shadowy yard,
crying heartily by the time he reached the veranda so that when he
flung himself at the white pillar and bawled, 'Den! Den! Den!' his
voice broke with rage and pity at the disgrace of it all and he felt
himself flooded with tears and misery.

220 Out on the lawn, the children stopped chanting. They all turned to
stare at him in amazement. Their faces were pale and triangular in the
dusk. The trees and bushes around them stood inky and sepulchral,
spilling long shadows across them. They stared, wondering at his
reappearance, his passion, his wild animal howling. Their mother rose
225 from her basket chair and came towards him, worried, annoyed,
saying, 'Stop it, stop it, Ravi. Don't be a baby. Have you hurt yourself?'
Seeing him attended to, the children went back to clasping their
hands and chanting 'The grass is green, the rose is red . . .'

But Ravi would not let them. He tore himself out of his mother's
230 grasp and pounded across the lawn into their midst, charging at them
with his head lowered so that they scattered in surprise. 'I won, I
won, I won,' he bawled, shaking his head so that the big tears flew.

'Raghu didn't find me. I won, I won – '

235 It took them a minute to grasp what he was saying, even who he was. They had quite forgotten him. Raghu had found all the others long ago. There had been a fight about who was to be It next. It had been so fierce that their mother had emerged from her bath and made them change to another game. Then they had played another and

240 another. Broken mulberries from the tree and eaten them. Helped the driver wash the car when their father returned from work. Helped the gardener water the beds till he roared at them and swore he would complain to their parents. The parents had come out, taken up their positions on the cane chairs. They had begun to play again, sing and chant. All this time no one had remembered Ravi. Having disappeared

245 from the scene, he had disappeared from their minds. Clean.

'Don't be a fool,' Raghu said roughly, pushing him aside, and even Mira said, 'Stop howling, Ravi. If you want to play, you can stand at the end of the line,' and she put him there very firmly.

The game proceeded. Two pairs of arms reached up and met in an
250 arc. The children trooped under it again and again in a lugubrious circle, ducking their heads and intoning

'The grass is green,

The rose is red;

Remember me
255 When I am dead, dead, dead, dead . . .'

And the arc of thin arms trembled in the twilight, and the heads were bowed so sadly, and their feet tramped to that melancholy refrain so mournfully, so helplessly, that Ravi could not bear it. He would not follow them, he would not be included in this funereal

260 game. He had wanted victory and triumph – not a funeral. But he had been forgotten, left out and he would not join them now. The ignominy of being forgotten – how could he face it? He felt his heart go heavy and ache inside him unbearably. He lay down full length on the damp grass, crushing his face into it, no longer crying, silenced by

265 a terrible sense of his insignificance.

Yuri Nagibin

RUSSIA

The Winter Oak

Yuri Nagibin was born in Moscow in 1924. He was best known for his short stories, which include 'Komaro', 'A Girl and an Echo' and 'The Whip'. The themes explored by Nagibin range from war and rural life, to history and music. He wrote scripts for a number of films, such as *The Chairman*, about life on a collective farm, which became a legend of national Russian cinema. Nagibin died in 1994.

The piercing bell that announced the beginning of the school day had hardly died down when Anna Vasilevna came into the class-room. The children stood up in a friendly way to greet her, and then settled down in their places. Quiet was not immediately

5 established. There was a banging of desk lids and a squeaking of benches, and someone sighed noisily, apparently bidding farewell to the serenity of the morning atmosphere.

'Today we are going to continue learning about parts of speech.'

The class quietened down, and a heavy lorry with a trailer could

10 be heard crawling along the road.

Anna Vasilevna remembered how last year she used to worry before a lesson, and would repeat to herself like a schoolgirl at an examination, 'The noun is that part of speech . . . the noun is that part of speech . . .'. And she remembered too how she used to be

15 tormented by a ridiculous fear that perhaps they would not understand her.

Anna Vasilevna smiled at this memory, pushed a hairpin back into her heavy knot of hair, and, conscious of the self-control which spread like warmth through her whole body, began in a calm voice:

20 'The word *noun* is used for that part of speech which is the subject. In grammar the subject is what we call everything about which we can ask, who is this, or what is this. For instance: "Who is this?" – "A pupil." Or: "What is this?" – "A book."'

'May I come in?' A small figure in worn felt boots and covered in

25 sparklets of frost that were thawing and losing their brightness stood
by the half-open door. The round face was burning and as red from
the frost as if it had been rubbed with beetroot, while the eyebrows
were grey with rime.

'Late again, Savushkin?' Like most young teachers, Anna Vasilevna
30 enjoyed being stern, but on this occasion her question sounded
plaintive.

Assuming that the schoolmistress's words gave him permission to
enter the class-room, Savushkin quickly slipped into his place. Anna
Vasilevna saw the boy push his oil-cloth bag into his desk, and,
35 without turning his head, say something to his neighbour, presumably
asking what she was explaining.

Anna Vasilevna was disappointed by Savushkin's lateness; it was
an unfortunate mishap spoiling a day that had begun well. She had
had complaints about Savushkin being late from the geography
40 mistress, a shrivelled little old woman who looked like a moth.
Actually she often complained – of noisy classes and inattentive
pupils. 'The first lesson is so difficult,' the old woman would sigh. 'It
is, for those who cannot control the children and make the lesson
interesting,' Anna Vasilevna thought to herself with self-assurance, and
45 offered to exchange periods. She now felt guilty towards the old lady,
who was sufficiently perceptive to recognize the challenge and
rebuke in Anna Vasilevna's amicable suggestion.

'Do you all understand?' Anna Vasilevna asked, addressing herself
to the class.

50 'Yes, yes,' chorused the children.

'Good. Now give me some examples.'

There was absolute silence for some seconds, and then someone
said uncertainly:

'Cat.'

55 'Right,' said Anna Vasilevna, immediately remembering that last
year the first example had also been 'cat'. And then there was an
outburst.

'Window! Table! House! Road!'

'Right,' Anna Vasilevna went on saying.

60 The class bubbled happily. Anna Vasilevna was surprised by the

delight with which the children named familiar objects, recognizing, as it were, their new and unaccustomed significance. The range of examples went on widening, but in the first minutes the children stuck to what was closest to them, to tangible objects – wheel, tractor,

65   well, starling-house.

From a desk at the back where fat Vasyata sat there came a high persistent voice:

'Nail . . . nail . . . nail.'

Then someone said timidly:

70   'Town.'

'Town, that's good,' said Anna Vasilevna approvingly.

And then the words began to fly:

'Street, metro, tram, film.'

'That's enough,' said Anna Vasilevna. 'I see you understand.'

75   Rather unwillingly the voices fell silent; only fat Vasyata went on muttering his unacknowledged 'nail'. Suddenly, just as if he had woken up out of a dream, Savushkin stood up in his desk, and shouted out in a ringing tone:

'Winter oak.'

80   The children began to laugh.

'Quiet,' said Anna Vasilevna, banging the table with her hand.

'Winter oak,' Savushkin repeated, noticing neither the laughter of his schoolfellows, nor the teacher's admonishment. He did not speak as the other children had. The words were torn out of his soul, like a

85   confession, or a joyful secret which he could not keep from spilling out of his heart.

Not understanding his strange excitement, Anna Vasilevna hid her irritation with difficulty, and said:

'Why winter? Just oak.'

90   'No, not just oak. Winter oak, that's the noun!'

'Sit down, Savushkin; this is what happens when you are late. "Oak" is a noun, and we have not yet come to what "winter" would be. Kindly come and see me in the staff-room during break.'

'There's winter oak for you,' someone sniggered from a back desk.

95   Savushkin sat down, smiling, at his own thoughts, and not in the least perturbed by the teacher's threatening words. 'A difficult boy,'

thought Anna Vasilevna.

The lesson continued.

'Sit down,' said Anna Vasilevna when Savushkin came into the
100 staff-room.

The boy sank into an armchair with pleasure, and bounced up and
down on the springs a few times.

'Kindly explain why you are consistently late.'

'I really don't know, Anna Vasilevna,' he said, spreading out his
105 hands in a grown-up way. 'I leave home an hour beforehand.'

How difficult it is to get at the truth in the very simplest matter!
Many of the children lived much farther away than Savushkin, and yet
none of them spent more than an hour getting to school.

'You live at Kuzminki?'

110 'No, by the sanatorium.'

'Are you not ashamed to say that you leave home an hour before
school starts? It takes fifteen minutes to get from the sanatorium to the
road, and then not more than half an hour to walk along the road.'

'I don't go along the road. I go the short way, straighting through
115 the forest,' said Savushkin, as if this circumstance surprised him.

'Not straighting, straight,' Anna Vasilevna corrected automatically.

She felt sad and confused as she always did when faced with a
child telling lies. She was silent, hoping that Savushkin would say,
'I'm sorry, Anna Vasilevna, I was snowballing with some boys,' or
120 something equally simple and innocent, but he only looked at her
with big grey eyes and his expression seemed to be saying, 'There
now, it has all been explained. What else do you want of me?'

'It's a pity, Savushkin, a great pity! I shall have to speak to your
parents.'

125 'I've only got a mother,' said Savushkin smiling.

'I'll have to call on your mother.'

'Do come and see her, Anna Vasilevna. My mother will be
pleased.'

'Unfortunately, I have nothing to say that will give her any
130 pleasure. Does your mother work in the mornings?'

'No, she's on the second shift, from three o'clock.'

'Well, that's good. I am free at two. When lessons are over, you will take me home.'

The path along which Savushkin led Anna Vasilevna began just
135 behind the school building. As soon as they stepped into the forest
and the fir branches that looked like paws heavily laden with snow
closed behind them, they were immediately transported into another
world, an enchanted world of peace and silence. Magpies and crows
flew from tree to tree, shaking the branches, knocking off the fir
140 cones, and sometimes their wings caught on the dry, brittle twigs, and
broke them. Yet not a sound could be heard.

All around everything was white. Only high up the wind had
blown on the tops of the soaring weeping birches, so that they
showed up black, and their delicate little branches looked as if they
145 had been etched in Indian ink on the blue surface of the sky.

The path ran by the stream, sometimes alongside it, submissively
following its twisting course, sometimes rising high up and winding
along a steep bank.

Now and again the trees would part and reveal sunny, joyful
150 glades, criss-crossed with hare tracks that looked like watch-chains.
There would also be heavier tracks shaped like a trefoil, and they
must have been made by a larger beast. These tracks ran right into the
thicket, in among tree-trunks that had fallen to the wind.

'An elk has been here,' said Savushkin, as if talking about a close
155 friend, when he saw that Anna Vasilevna was interested in the tracks.
'But don't be afraid,' he added in response to the glance the
schoolmistress threw towards the depths of the forest, 'the deer is
gentle.'

'Have you seen one?' asked Anna Vasilevna excitedly.

160 'No,' – Savushkin sighed. 'I haven't actually seen one, not alive.
But I've seen his pellets.'

'Pellets?'

'Droppings,' Savushkin explained shyly.

Slipping under an archway of bent branches, the path again ran
165 down to the stream. In some places the stream was covered with a
thick white blanket of snow, while in others it was imprisoned in an
armour of clear ice, and sometimes living water would gleam through
the ice, looking like a dark, malevolent eye.

'Why has it not all frozen up?' asked Anna Vasilevna.

170   'There's a warm spring which rises up in it. Look! See that little jet?'

Bending over an unfrozen patch in the middle of the ice, Anna Vasilevna could see a thin little thread rising up from the bottom; by the time it reached the surface it had broken into tiny bubbles. This minute stem with the little bubbles on it looked like a spray of lily of

175 the valley.

'There are loads of springs like that here,' said Savushkin enthusiastically. 'The stream is alive even under the snow.'

He brushed away the snow, and they saw the coal-black but transparent water.

180 Anna Vasilevna noticed that, when the snow fell into the water, it did not melt away, but immediately turned into slush, a greenish jelly suspended in the water as if it were algae. She was so pleased with this that she began to kick snow into the water with the toe of her boot, and was enraptured when a particularly intricate figure emerged

185 from a large lump of snow. She was so enthralled that she did not at once notice that Savushkin had gone on, and was waiting for her, sitting high up in the fork of a bough overhanging the stream. Anna Vasilevna caught him up. Here the action of the warm springs came to an end, and the stream was covered with a thin film of ice. Light

190 shadows darted rapidly over the marble surface.

'Look, the ice is so thin that we can even see the current!'

'No, Anna Vasilevna, I'm swaying this branch, and that's its shadow moving.'

Anna Vasilevna bit her tongue. Clearly here in the forest she had

195 better keep quiet.

Savushkin strode on again in front of the schoolmistress, bending down slightly and looking around him.

And the forest led them on still farther along its intricate, tangled paths. It seemed as if there was no end to the trees, the snowdrifts

200 and the silence of the sun-dappled twilight.

Suddenly, in the distance, a smoky-blue chink appeared. The trees began to thin out, there was more space and it was fresher. Soon there was no longer a chink, but a broad shaft of sunlight appeared before them, and in it something glistened and sparkled, swarming

205 with frosty stars.

The path went round a hazel bush, and straightaway the forest fell away on either side. In the middle of the glade, clothed in glittering white raiment, huge and majestic as a cathedral, stood an oak. It seemed as if the trees had respectfully stood aside to give their older
210 brother room to display himself in all his strength. The lower branches spread out over the glade like a canopy.

Snow was packed into the deep corrugations of the bark, and the trunk, three times the normal girth, seemed to be embroidered with silver thread. Few of the leaves that had withered in the autumn had
215 fallen, and the oak was covered right up to the top with leaves encased in snow.

'There it is, the winter oak!'

Anna Vasilevna approached the oak timidly, and the mighty, magnanimous guardian of the forest quietly waved a branch in
220 greeting to her.

Savushkin had no idea what was going on in the schoolmistress's heart, and he busied himself at the foot of the oak, as if approaching an old acquaintance.

'Look, Anna Vasilevna!'

225 He had managed to drag away a lump of snow that had stuck to the ground and was covered with the remains of dead grass. There, in a little hollow, lay a ball wrapped in rotted leaves as thin as spiders' webs. Sharp-tipped quills stuck out through the leaves. Anna Vasilevna guessed that this was a hedgehog.

230 'See how he has muffled himself up!'

Savushkin carefully covered the hedgehog up with his unpretentious blanket. Then he scraped away the snow from another root to reveal a tiny grotto, with a bunch of icicles hanging from its roof. A brown frog was sitting inside; it could have been made of
235 cardboard, and its skin, tightly drawn over its bone structure, might have been lacquered. Savushkin touched the frog, but it did not move.

'It's pretending to be dead,' said Savushkin laughing. 'But just let the sun warm it, and you'll see how it hops about!'

240 He went on showing Anna Vasilevna his own small world.

A number of other lodgers – beetles, lizards and small insects – had taken refuge at the foot of the oak. Some had buried themselves under the roots, others had wriggled into crevices in the bark; emaciated, practically hollow inside, they were surviving the winter in
245 a sleep from which they could not be woken. The mighty tree, laden with life, had gathered so much living warmth round itself that the poor creatures could not have found a better lodging. Anna Vasilevna was gazing with delighted interest at this secret forest life, hitherto unknown to her, when she heard Savushkin exclaim in concern:
250 'Oh, we'll miss mother now!'

Anna Vasilevna hurriedly looked at her watch – it was a quarter past three. She felt as if she had walked into a trap. Privately asking the oak to forgive her for being human and slightly cunning, she said:

'Well, Savushkin, this just shows that the short cut is not always the
255 surest. You'll have to go by the road.'

Savushkin did not say anything; he just hung his head.

'Heavens,' thought Anna Vasilevna painfully, 'could one have shown one's incompetence more clearly?' She remembered the lesson that day, and all her other lessons: how inadequately, drily and coldly
260 she had spoken of words and language, without which man is dumb and powerless to express his feelings before the world, when all the time her own native tongue was as fresh, beautiful and rich as life is generous and beautiful.

And she had considered herself an able teacher! Quite possibly she
265 had not yet taken the first step along that road which takes more than a whole life to traverse. And how can one find that road? Perhaps the first signpost was dimly visible in the delight, incomprehensible to her at the time, with which the children shouted out 'tractor', 'well', 'starling-house'.
270 'Well, Savushkin, thank you for the walk. Of course you can come this way.'

'Thank you, Anna Vasilevna.'

Savushkin blushed; he very much wanted to say to the schoolmistress that he would never be late again, but he was afraid of
275 telling a lie. He turned up the collar of his jacket and pulled down his cap with the ear flaps.

'I'll see you home.'

'You needn't, Savushkin. I'll go by myself.'

He looked at the schoolmistress doubtfully, and then he picked up
280 a stick from the ground, broke off its crooked end and gave the stick
to Anna Vasilevna.

'If the elk comes near you, hit him on the back, and he'll run
away. Or better still, just wave the stick at him, and that will be
enough. Otherwise he might take offence and leave the forest
285 altogether.'

'All right, Savushkin, I won't hit him.'

When she had gone a little way, Anna Vasilevna turned round to
have a last look at the oak, rosy white in the setting sun, and at its
foot she saw a small, dark figure. Savushkin had not gone home. He
290 was guarding his teacher from afar. And suddenly Anna Vasilevna
understood that the most amazing thing in the forest was not the
winter oak, but the small human being in the worn felt boots, a
mysterious and wonderful future citizen.

She waved to him and quietly went off along the twisting path.

Acknowledgements

The Publishers wish to thank the following, who have kindly granted permission for the use of copyright material:

'Dead Men's Path' by Chinua Achebe, published by Heinemann Educational. Reprinted with permission of REPP; 'Snapshots of a Wedding' by Bessie Head, published by Heinemann Educational. Reprinted with permission of REPP; 'The Train from Rhodesia' by Nadine Gordimer, from *Selected Stories*, published by Jonathan Cape. Reprinted with permission of A. P. Watt Limited on behalf of Nadine Gordimer; 'The Gold-Legged Frog' translated by Domern Garden, from *The Politician and Other Stories*, published by Silkworm Books. Reprinted with permission of the author and Silkworm Books; 'Two Kinds' by Amy Tan, from *The Joy Luck Club*, © 1989 Amy Tan. Reprinted with permission of Abner Stein; 'The Tall Woman and Her Short Husband' by Feng Ji-Cai, translated by Gladys Yang, © English Translation Gladys Yang. Reprinted with permission of Yang Zhi (daughter of Gladys Yang); 'The Pieces of Silver' by Karl Sealy. Reprinted with kind permission of Beryl Sealy, wife of the late Karl Sealy; 'The Red Ball' by Ismith Khan, from *A Day in the Country* by Ismith Khan, published by Peepal Tree Press, 1994. Reprinted with permission of the publishers; 'The Young Couple' by Ruth Prawer Jhabvala, from *A Stronger Climate*, published by John Murray (Publishers) Limited. Reprinted with permission of the publishers; 'Leela's Friend' by R. K. Narayan, from *Malgudi Days*, first published in Great Britain by William Heinemann in 1982. Copyright © 1972, 1975, 1978, 1980, 1981, 1982 by R. K. Narayan. Reprinted with permission of Sheil Land Associates Limited; 'Games at Twilight' by Anita Desai, from *Games At Twilight*, first published by Vintage. Copyright © Anita Desai 1978. Reproduced by permission of Rogers Coleridge & White Limited, 20 Powis Mews, London W11 1JN.

Whilst every effort has been made to locate the owners of copyright, in some cases this has been unsuccessful. The publishers apologise for any omission of original sources and will be pleased to make the necessary arrangements at the first opportunity.